Y0-CAX-026

Using This Book

Daily Practice

Did you know that vocabulary development is linked to improved reading comprehension? In this reproducible book you'll find daily vocabulary practice with essential fourth-grade words. It's a valuable classroom resource packed with quick and easy-to-use activities designed to strengthen vocabulary and build better readers. You can use these activities in a variety of classroom situations—as daily warm-ups, quick assessment tools, or helpful reviews.

The book's organization features 36 weekly practice sessions, followed by a monthly review of words covered in the previous weeks. This approach allows for in-depth and focused practice of essential vocabulary words in a concentrated time frame. This engaging resource provides high-interest content and vocabulary practice in context.

The exercises offered in the first part of each week are simpler. These afford students the opportunity to experience success while practicing previously introduced vocabulary words. As the week progresses, the activities gradually become more challenging. Likewise, the more challenging vocabulary words are offered as the year progresses.

Later sections of the book are directly related to fourth-grade content areas including science, mathematics, language arts, and social studies. You might plan to use these sections to complement content-area studies, bearing in mind that through repetition and repeated exposure students' vocabulary grows. It's one more way for students to practice material recently taught and for you to assess students' progress.

When planning your daily routine, try one or more of these management techniques:

- You might choose to have students work together for Day One through Day Three and then individually for Days Four and Five. When students work independently, encourage them to exchange work with a partner and compare and discuss their answers. Or, review the correct responses together as a large group.
- Use an overhead projector or create transparencies to complete the work in a large group. Ask volunteers to help complete each item. Try completing Day One as a whole-class activity to review the day's vocabulary words. Then have students work independently or in pairs throughout the week.
- Use the workbook to complement content area studies. For example, you might have students conclude a lesson on the branches of government by completing the corresponding pages in the practice book.

Weekly Reviews

There is a weekly review to reinforce the work of previous days. You can use these reviews as an assessment, collecting each student's work individually. You might prefer to use the vocabulary review as an assessment tool to determine which words students still need to practice.

Monthly Reviews

At the end of each four-week set there is an activity page that reviews the skills taught during that month. Each monthly review includes word searches, crossword puzzles, and other engaging word games.

Extensions & Activities

Helping your students develop and build a strong vocabulary is an ongoing process. This activity book is a terrific tool to help you reach your educational goals. But it's not the only thing you can do every day to help students develop a strong vocabulary. Here's what you can do:

Use the vocabulary words in everyday speech. As you use this daily practice book make it a point to use the words in conversation. For example, instead of telling students that you are going to show them how to use a computer program, say that you will demonstrate how the program works. In this way, you are reinforcing the word, integrating it in a practical way and giving an example of how the word is used in context.

Read aloud to students. Reading aloud from authentic literature is an essential tool for vocabulary development. By reading aloud, you are introducing students to rich language. You can also reinforce important vocabulary words by engaging students in a book talk, focusing on words you want your students to know.

You can create additional learning opportunities by incorporating vocabulary words into teacher-created games and activities. Here are some suggestions:

Word of the Day Challenge students to incorporate the word into their everyday speech. At the end of the day, ask students to give examples of how and when the word was used.

Synonym Concentration Have students choose five words. They should write each word and one synonym for each word on separate note cards for a total of 10 cards. Working with a partner, students should then arrange the cards face down. Students will then take turns turning over two cards at a time, trying to match the synonyms in the set. The game can also be played using antonyms.

Compound Words Write compound words on note cards, then cut the cards in half to form two separate words. Shuffle the cards, then have students put them back together to form compound words.

Super Sentences Challenge students to use the weekly vocabulary words in a sentence. Encourage them to use not just one of the words in each sentence, but several.

Wacky Word Searches Have students create their own word searches. Give each student a 10 x 10 grid on which to create the word search. Then, students should exchange their puzzles with a partner and complete the puzzle. There are also several online programs designed to help students create word searches.

Homophone Bingo Have students brainstorm a list of homophones. Then, use the words to prepare BINGO cards. Instead of calling out a letter/number combination as you would in a traditional BINGO game use one of the homophones in a sentence. Students then must identify the word in context and find its match on their BINGO board.

Silly Sentences Read sentences to students. Then, have students replace words with antonyms in order to create a silly sentence. For example, a student might respond to the sentence "I am so tired I can barely stay awake" by saying "I am so alert I can barely stay asleep."

DAILY VOCABULARY PRACTICE

Nouns

1

Name ______________________________

A common noun names a general person, place, or thing. *President*, *state*, and *bridge* are common nouns. A proper noun names a specific person, place, or thing. *Abraham Lincoln*, *California*, and *Brooklyn Bridge* are proper nouns.

Is it a noun? Write yes or no on the line.

1. paper ____________
2. dictionary ____________
3. write ____________
4. glued ____________
5. Sarah Henderson ____________

nouns verbs adverbs adjectives Week One

DAILY VOCABULARY PRACTICE

Nouns

2

Name ______________________________

A common noun names a general person, place, or thing. *President*, *state*, and *bridge* are common nouns. A proper noun names a specific person, place, or thing. *Abraham Lincoln*, *California*, and *Brooklyn Bridge* are proper nouns.

Match the common noun on the left with the proper noun on the right.

1. park	St. Luke's Medical Center
2. street	Empire State Building
3. building	Main Street
4. hospital	Yosemite National Park
5. train station	Grand Central Station

Nouns

3

Name ______________________________

A common noun names a general person, place, or thing. *President*, *state*, and *bridge* are common nouns. A proper noun names a specific person, place, or thing. *Abraham Lincoln*, *California*, and *Brooklyn Bridge* are proper nouns.

Read each sentence. Circle common nouns. Underline proper nouns.

1. Mr. Gonzalez is a teacher.
2. He teaches at a school called Learning Academy.
3. Mr. Gonzalez has 25 students in his class.
4. The class is studying Native Americans.
5. Students will learn about the Navajo Indians.

ouns verbs adverbs adjectives Week One
DAILY VOCABULARY PRACTICE

Nouns

4

Name ______________________________

A common noun names a general person, place, or thing. *President*, *state*, and *bridge* are common nouns. A proper noun names a specific person, place, or thing. *Abraham Lincoln*, *California*, and *Brooklyn Bridge* are proper nouns.

Read the sentences. Fill in the blanks with the missing nouns.

Each year, school starts at the beginning of ______________________.

In ______________________, we will have winter vacation.

We will celebrate New Year's Day on the first of ______________________.

Spring vacation is in the middle of ______________________.

______________________ 21st is the first day of summer.

December	January	June	March	September

© Weekly Reader Corporation

DAILY VOCABULARY PRACTICE

Nouns

5

Name ______________________________

A common noun names a general person, place, or thing. *President*, *state*, and *bridge* are common nouns. A proper noun names a specific person, place, or thing. *Abraham Lincoln*, *California*, and *Brooklyn Bridge* are proper nouns.

Unscramble each common noun. Write each word on the line.

1. uyabte ______________________
2. pacee ______________________
3. nlilgeitcnee ______________________
4. oevl ______________________
5. hntyeso ______________________

love beauty peace honesty intelligence

DAILY VOCABULARY PRACTICE

Nouns

Name ______________________________

Read each common noun. Choose the best proper noun to go with it.

1. state ______________________
2. apple ______________________
3. ocean ______________________
4. volcano ______________________
5. author ______________________

Arctic Arizona Golden Delicious J.K. Rowling Vesuvius

Verbs

1

Name ______________________________

A verb is an action word. *Walk* is a verb. *Read* is a verb. *Organize* is a verb.

Is it a verb? Circle yes or no.

1. run **yes** **no**
2. point **yes** **no**
3. children **yes** **no**
4. American **yes** **no**
5. listen **yes** **no**

nouns verbs adverbs adjectives Week Two
DAILY VOCABULARY PRACTICE

Verbs

2

Name ______________________________

A verb is an action word. *Walk* is a verb. *Read* is a verb. *Organize* is a verb.

Choose the best verb to complete each sentence.

1. ______________________ your fingers with the music.
2. ______________________ the drum softly.
3. ______________________ your toes in time with the beat.
4. ______________________ a song for me.
5. ______________________ your hands five times.

beat	**clap**	**sing**	**snap**	**tap**

DAILY VOCABULARY PRACTICE

Verbs

3

Name ______________________________

A verb is an action word. *Realize* is a verb. *Grow* is a verb. *Organize* is a verb.

Choose a verb from the word box to complete each sentence.

1. Our class will ____________________ the library each Tuesday.
2. The librarian will ____________________ how to use the new computers.
3. She will ____________________ us new tricks for searching on the Internet.
4. We will ____________________ the library's online catalog.
5. Each student will ____________________ which book to check out.

decide	demonstrate	search	teach	visit

nouns verbs adverbs adjectives Week Two

DAILY VOCABULARY PRACTICE

Verbs

Name ______________________________

A verb is an action word. *Realize* is a verb. *Grow* is a verb. *Organize* is a verb.

Fill in the missing vowels to complete each verb. Check the word box for hints.

1. s ______ pp ______ rt
2. ______ dent ______ fy
3. r ______ ______ l ______ z ______
4. c ______ mpr ______ h ______ nd
5. ______ bs ______ rv ______

comprehend	identify	observe	realize	support

DAILY VOCABULARY PRACTICE

Verbs

5

Name ______________________________

A verb is an action word. *Realize* is a verb. *Grow* is a verb. *Organize* is a verb.

Sometimes the same word can be a verb or a noun. It depends how it is used. Read each sentence. Is the boldface word used as a noun or adverb? Circle your answer.

1. The **show** starts at seven o'clock.	**Noun**	**Verb**
2. The usher will **show** us to our seats.	**Noun**	**Verb**
3. My mother will **play** the part of Lady MacBeth.	**Noun**	**Verb**
4. The first act of the **play** is set in England.	**Noun**	**Verb**
5. The show will **play** three more times this week.	**Noun**	**Verb**

DAILY VOCABULARY PRACTICE

Verbs

Name ______________________________

Circle the verb (or verbs) in each sentence.

1. Consider your choices.
2. Devon will increase the number of miles she runs each week.
3. Please distribute the papers.
4. José volunteers to read to younger children.
5. Imagine what the trip will be like.

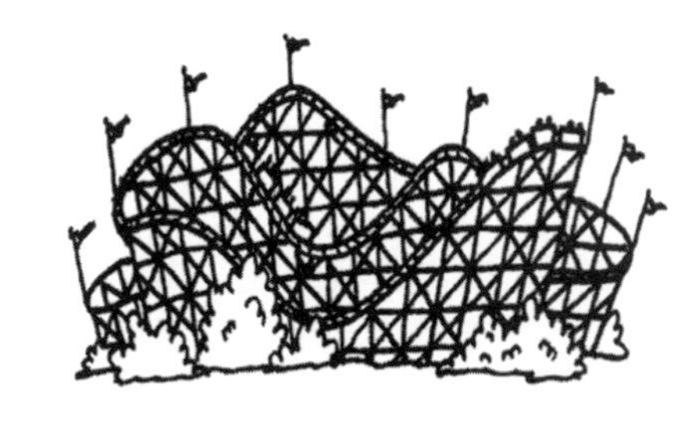

DAILY VOCABULARY PRACTICE

Adjectives

1

Name ______________________

An adjective is a word used to describe a noun. For example, *red, crunchy,* and *sweet* are adjectives that could be used to describe an apple.

Underline the adjectives in each sentence.

1. Last night I ate a delicious meal.
2. My sister Margie made Italian food.
3. We ate crusty bread and crunchy salad.
4. We had curly pasta topped with a chunky sauce.
5. For dessert we ate sweet oranges and creamy cheesecake.

DAILY VOCABULARY PRACTICE

Adjectives

2

Name ______________________

An adjective is a word used to describe a noun. For example: *red, crunchy,* and *sweet* are adjectives that could be used to describe an apple.

Choose the best adjective from the word box to complete each *hink pink* rhyme.

1. A ______________________ rabbit is a funny bunny.
2. A ______________________ town is a pretty city.
3. A ______________________ mammal is an eager beaver.
4. An ______________________ insect is a free bee.
5. An ______________________ postcard is a better letter.

beautiful **curious** **hilarious** **improved** **independent**

Adjectives

3

Name ______________________________

An adjective is a word used to describe a noun. For example, *red, crunchy,* and *sweet* are adjectives that could be used to describe an apple.

Match each adjective with its definition.

1. clever	smart
2. anxious	happy
3. ecstatic	playful
4. cooperative	worried
5. mischievous	helpful

Adjectives

Name ______________________________

An adjective is a word used to describe a noun. For example, *red, crunchy,* and *sweet* are adjectives that could be used to describe an apple.

Unscramble the adjectives in each sentence.

1. John wore a ykubl ______________________ ski jacket.
2. Germs are so small they are poisccormic ______________________.
3. amsisve ______________________ chunks of ice broke off the glacier.
4. A billion dollars is an meismne ______________________ amount of money.
5. The ship model was a tmiuainre ______________________ version of a real clipper ship.

bulky	**immense**	**massive**	**microscopic**	**miniature**

DAILY VOCABULARY PRACTICE

Adjectives

5

Name ________________________________

An adjective is a word used to describe a noun. For example, *red, crunchy,* and *sweet* are adjectives that could be used to describe an apple.

Read each set of words. Circle the adjective.

1. delicious	decide	determine
2. ribbon	ridiculous	riddle
3. ancient	age	angle
4. modem	modify	modern
5. insist	insistent	invite

DAILY VOCABULARY PRACTICE

Adjectives

Name ________________________________

Select the *best* adjective to describe each item on the list. Use each word in the word bank only once.

1. a world traveler ____________________
2. a work of art ____________________
3. a football stadium ____________________
4. a circus elephant ____________________
5. a friend ____________________

enormous original reliable vast weary

DAILY VOCABULARY PRACTICE

Adverbs

1

Name ____________________________

Adverbs modify verbs and adjectives. They tell how, why, when and where. In the sentence, "The girl ran quickly down the stairs," *quickly* modifies the word *ran*. It tells how the girl ran.

Change each adjective into an adverb by adding the suffix –ly. Write each new word on the line.

1. elegant ____________________
2. faithful ____________________
3. courageous ____________________
4. successful ____________________
5. innocent ____________________

ouns verbs adverbs adjectives Week Four

DAILY VOCABULARY PRACTICE

Adverbs

2

Name ____________________________

Adverbs modify verbs and adjectives. They tell how, why, when and where. In the sentence, "The girl ran quickly down the stairs," *quickly* modifies the word *ran*. It tells how the girl ran.

The suffix –ly can be added to nouns to indicate how often something is done. Add the –ly to each word. Write the new word on the line.

1. hour ____________________
2. day ____________________
3. week ____________________
4. month ____________________
5. year ____________________

Hint:
Simply adding –ly to day will not work! Change the letter *y* to *i* to correctly spell the adverb.

DAILY VOCABULARY PRACTICE

Adverbs

3

Name ______________________________

Adverbs modify verbs and adjectives. They tell how, why, when and where. In the sentence, "The girl ran quickly down the stairs," *quickly* modifies the word *ran*. It tells how the girl ran.

Circle the adverb in each sentence. Underline the word that it modifies.

1. The horse galloped swiftly through the field.
2. The cat approached the mouse slowly.
3. The dog jumped playfully into the air.
4. The hamster happily nibbled the carrot.
5. The bear slept peacefully in its den.

nouns verbs adverbs adjectives Week Four

DAILY VOCABULARY PRACTICE

Adverbs

Name ______________________________

Adverbs modify verbs and adjectives. They tell how, why, when and where. In the sentence, "The girl ran quickly down the stairs," *quickly* modifies the word *ran*. It tells how the girl ran.

Choose the best adverb to complete each sentence.

1. The young violin player is ______________________ talented.
2. After petting the farm animals, Lisa ______________________ washed her hands.
3. It rains ______________________ in Seattle, Washington.
4. The library is ______________________ located inside the school.
5. The guests arrived ______________________ at 8:00.

conveniently	**extremely**	**frequently**	**promptly**	**thoroughly**

DAILY VOCABULARY PRACTICE

Adverbs

5

Name ______________________________

Adverbs modify verbs and adjectives. They tell how, why, when and where. In the sentence, "The girl ran quickly down the stairs," *quickly* modifies the word *ran*. It tells how the girl ran.

Choose the best adverb to add to each sentence. Write the new sentence on the line.

1. Josh is late for school. ______________________________.
2. Help is needed! ______________________________.
3. The shirt is stained. ______________________________.
4. Most students worked ______________________________.
5. The parents met with the teacher ______________________________.

briefly independently occasionally permanently urgently

DAILY VOCABULARY PRACTICE

Adverbs

Name ______________________________

Choose the best adverb to complete each sentence.

1. If something disappears in a suspenseful way, it disappears ______________________.

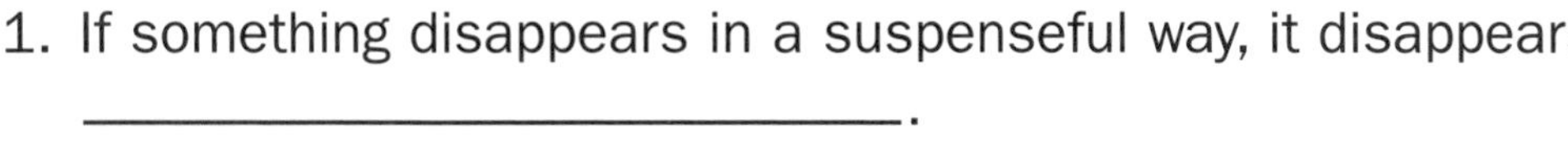

2. If you look at a person in a very respectful manner, you look at that person ______________________.
3. If you dance in a quick, bouncy way, you dance ______________________.
4. If a baby sleeps in a calm manner, the baby sleeps ______________________.
5. If you act in a sure, certain manner, you act ______________________.

decisively	adoringly	mysteriously	energetically	serenely

DAILY VOCABULARY PRACTICE

Name ______________________________

A. Fill in the bubble that matches each word.

1. curious ○ noun ○ verb ○ adverb ○ adjective
2. Empire State Building ○ noun ○ verb ○ adverb ○ adjective
3. innocently ○ noun ○ verb ○ adverb ○ adjective
4. demonstrate ○ noun ○ verb ○ adverb ○ adjective
5. independent ○ noun ○ verb ○ adverb ○ adjective

B. Circle each noun in the word find. Look across, up, down, and backwards. Write each noun on the line. Write a proper noun to go with it.

day month school street teacher

T	E	E	R	T	S
E	E	D	Q	L	H
A	Y	P	W	O	T
C	D	A	Y	O	N
H	F	B	N	H	O
E	X	E	L	C	M
R	V	R	F	S	E

nouns	proper nouns
____________	____________
____________	____________
____________	____________
____________	____________
____________	____________

C. Complete the puzzle

Across

1. What a __________ solution! So smart!
4. Are you __________ about starting school? Don't worry.
6. She arrived __________ at 9:00. She's always on time.
7. Help! I can't __________ what to wear to the party.

Down

3. The chef will __________ how to frost a cake.
2. You must __________ yourself to the guard before entering the building.
5. __________ to this great DVD!

promptly anxious clever decide listen demonstrate identify

Prefixes

1

Name ______________________________

A prefix is a group of letters added to the beginning of a word. A prefix changes or adds to the meaning of a word. The prefix *re–* means *to do again*.

Use the words from the word box to complete each sentence.

1. To ______________________ is to write something over again.
2. To ______________________ something is to put it back together.
3. To ______________________ something is to put it in a different order.
4. To ______________________ is to build something a second time.
5. To ______________________ is to find something all over again.

rearrange **reconstruct** **rediscover** **rewrite** **reassemble**

Prefixes

2

Name ______________________________

A prefix is a group of letters added to the beginning of a word. A prefix changes or adds to the meaning of a word. The prefixes *im–* and *in–* mean *not*.

Match each word with its definition.

1. cannot be done	immature
2. not nice; rude	impolite
3. unable to make a decision	impossible
4. not in need of outside help	indecisive
5. not fully grown	independent

DAILY VOCABULARY PRACTICE

Prefixes

3

Name ______________________________

A prefix is a group of letters added to the beginning of a word. A prefix changes or adds to the meaning of a word. The prefix *mis–* means *bad* or *wrong*.

Circle the word that makes the most sense with the phrase.

1. to make a poor judgment	**mistake**	**misjudge**
2. to give the wrong information	**misadventure**	**misinform**
3. to behave badly	**mistake**	**misbehave**
4. an accident	**mistake**	**miscalculate**
5. to check off numbers incorrectly	**miscount**	**misinform**

prefixes compound words suffixes base and root words Week Five

DAILY VOCABULARY PRACTICE

Prefixes

4

Name ______________________________

A prefix is a group of letters added to the beginning of a word. A prefix changes or adds to the meaning of a word. The prefix *uni–* means *one*, *bi–* means *two*, *tri–* means *three*, *dec–* means *ten*, and *cent–* means *one hundred*.

Read the clue. Write the answer on the line. Use the word box.

1. an Olympic sport with ten events ______________________
2. three babies born together ______________________
3. a cycle with one wheel ______________________
4. a 100–year period ______________________
5. a vehicle with two wheels ______________________

century	**decathlon**	**bicycle**	**triplets**	**unicycle**

DAILY VOCABULARY PRACTICE

Prefixes

5

Name ______________________________

A prefix is a group of letters added to the beginning of a word. A prefix changes or adds to the meaning of a word.

Match each prefix to a root to form a new word.

Prefix	+	Root Word	=	New Word
1. anti		scope		______________
2. post		social		______________
3. micro		pone		______________
4. mid		angle		______________
5. tri		night		______________

DAILY VOCABULARY PRACTICE

Prefixes

Name ______________________________

Circle the prefix in each word. Write the meaning of the word on the line.

1. reconstruct ______________________________
2. impolite ______________________________
3. miscalculate ______________________________
4. bicycle ______________________________
5. antisocial ______________________________

DAILY VOCABULARY PRACTICE

Suffixes

1

Name ______________________

A suffix is a group of letters added to the end of a word to change its meaning.

– ly	- ness	– ful	– less	– est

Choose suffixes from the list to add to each word. Write the new words on the lines. Some words can work with more than one suffix.

1. play ____________
2. quick ____________ ____________ ____________
3. help ____________ ____________
4. rest ____________ ____________
5. hard ____________ ____________ ____________

prefixes compound words suffixes base and root words Week Six

DAILY VOCABULARY PRACTICE

Suffixes

2

Name ______________________

A suffix is a group of letters added to the end of a word to change its meaning. The suffixes *–er* and *–est* help us to compare words.

Add the suffixes –er and –est to make comparison words.

1. brief ____________ ____________
2. late ____________ ____________
3. near ____________ ____________
4. high ____________ ____________
5. fast ____________ ____________

Hint:
If the word ends in e cut the e before adding the suffix.

Suffixes

3

Name ______________________________

A suffix is a group of letters added to the end of a word to change its meaning.

Suffix: –ive Meaning: likely to, inclined to

Choose the best word to complete each sentence. Circle the suffix.

1. The artist is full of ________________ ideas.
2. The ________________ solved the case.
3. The chef prepared a ________________ cake for 200 guests.
4. The football player made some ________________ moves on the field.
5. Animal experts say the wolf is a wild ________________ of the dog.

massive impressive creative detective relative

Suffixes

4

Name ______________________________

A suffix is a group of letters added to the end of a word to change its meaning. Add a suffix to each word to complete the sentence.

–ful –ness –ment –ly

1. Please arrive prompt________ at 8:00.
2. People have been eager________ waiting for the movie to be released.
3. The story is about a family that lives in the wilder________.
4. The audience was in agree________ on an important point.
5. One fan said that the movie was "just wonder________."

DAILY VOCABULARY PRACTICE

Suffixes

5

Name ________________________________

A suffix is a group of letters added to the end of a word to change its meaning.

Choose the best word ending to change each word from a verb to a noun.

Verb (action word)	Noun (person, place, or thing)
1. combine	________________
2. narrate	________________
3. define	________________
4. operate	________________
5. invite	________________

Hint: These words end with the letter e. To change the words into nouns you must drop the letter e.

–ion –ition –ation

DAILY VOCABULARY PRACTICE

Suffixes

Name ________________________________

Underline the suffixes in each pair of words.

1. agreeable agreement
2. eagerly eagerness
3. memorize memorable
4. formalize formalness
5. scarcely scarceness

Compound Words

1

Name ______________________________

A compound word is made of two words put together. *Outside* is a compound word. It's made of the words *out* and *side*. The words *foot* and *ball* form the word *football*.

Read each compound word. Draw a line to divide it into two separate words.

1. notebook
2. keyboard
3. download
4. desktop
5. password

Compound Words

2

Name ______________________________

A compound word is made of two words put together. *Outside* is a compound word. It's made of the words *out* and *side*. The words *foot* and *ball* form the word *football*.

Use the pictures to form a compound word.

1.  +  = ______________________
2.  +  = ______________________
3. 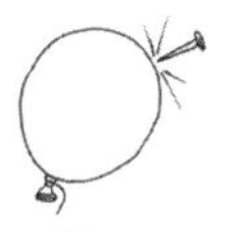 +  = ______________________
4.  +  = ______________________
5. + = ______________________

DAILY VOCABULARY PRACTICE

Compound Words

3

Name ______________________________

A compound word is made of two words put together. *Outside* is a compound word. It's made of the words *out* and *side*. The words *foot* and *ball* form the word *football*.

Write the compound word that best matches the description

1. a pleasant thought ____________________
2. something you find at the beach ____________________
3. a source of information ____________________
4. where you go for recess ____________________
5. heavy rainfall ____________________

daydream downpour newspaper playground seashell

prefixes compound words suffixes base and root words

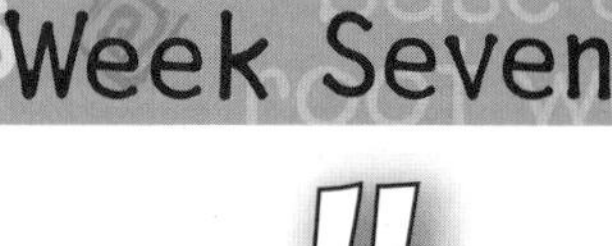

DAILY VOCABULARY PRACTICE

Compound Words

4

Name ______________________________

A compound word is made of two words put together. *Outside* is a compound word. It's made of the words *out* and *side*. The words *foot* and *ball* form the word *football*.

Match the words in each column to form compound words. Write the new words on the lines.

1. fore — ball ____________________
2. finger — head ____________________
3. eye — cap ____________________
4. back — nail ____________________
5. knee — bone ____________________

DAILY VOCABULARY PRACTICE

Compound Words

5

Name ____________________

A compound word is made of two words put together. *Outside* is a compound word. It's made of the words *out* and *side*. The words *foot* and *ball* form the word *football*.

Put these compound words in alphabetical order.

anywhere	somewhat	meanwhile	sometimes	another

1. ____________________
2. ____________________
3. ____________________
4. ____________________
5. ____________________

DAILY VOCABULARY PRACTICE

Compound Words

Name ____________________

Add another word to each line to make a compound word.

1. finger ____________________
2. cross ____________________
3. flash ____________________
4. head ____________________
5. spot ____________________

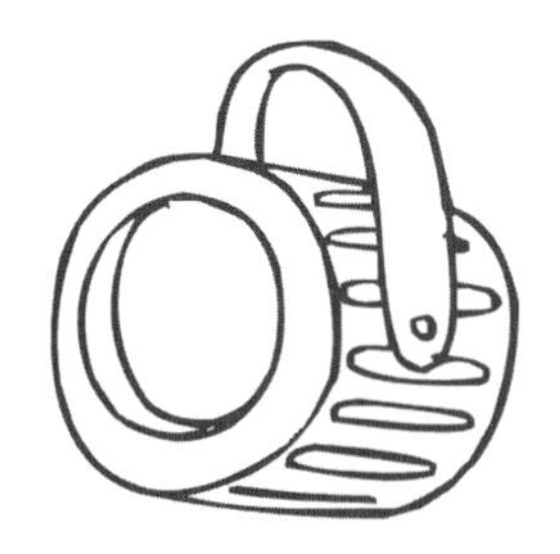

back	light	nail	quarters	walk

DAILY VOCABULARY PRACTICE

Base Words

1

Name ____________________________________

Base words can be used to grow other words. For example, *speedy and speedier* are two words that share the base word *speed*.

Underline the base word in each word.

1. unclear
2. useless
3. painful
4. kingdom
5. approve

DAILY VOCABULARY PRACTICE

Base Words

2

Name ____________________________________

Base words can be used to grow other words. For example, *speedy and speedier* are two words that share the base word *speed*.

Match each word with its base.

1. explanation	act
2. confusion	explain
3. action	form
4. formation	caution
5. precaution	confuse

DAILY VOCABULARY PRACTICE

Base Words

3

Name ______________________________

Base words can be used to grow other words. For example, *speedy and speedier* are two words that share the base word *speed*.

Choose a base word to add to each word ending. Make new words.

1. ______________________ ly
2. ______________________ ant
3. ______________________ ful
4. ______________________ ity
5. ______________________ ative

beauty	clear	electric	represent	triumph

prefixes compound words suffixes base and root words Week Eight

DAILY VOCABULARY PRACTICE

Base Words

Name ______________________________

Base words can be used to grow other words. For example, *speedy and speedier* are two words that share the base word *speed*.

Read each word. Write its base on the line.

1. unionize ______________________
2. relation ______________________
3. teacher ______________________
4. distinction ______________________
5. embarrassment ______________________

DAILY VOCABULARY PRACTICE

Base Words

5

Name ______________________________

Base words can be used to grow other words. For example, *speedy and speedier* are two words that share the base word *speed*.

Look at each word group. Which one is the base word? Write it on the line.

			Base Word
1. decision	decide	indecisive	____________
2. produce	production	producer	____________
3. additive	additional	add	____________
4. correction	correct	correctly	____________
5. completion	completely	complete	____________

DAILY VOCABULARY PRACTICE

Base Words

Name ______________________________

Circle the base in each word. Use the base to write a new word on the line.

1. incomplete ____________
2. acting ____________
3. embarrassing ____________
4. addition ____________
5. meaningless ____________

DAILY VOCABULARY PRACTICE

Name ______________________________

A. Choose the best word to complete each sentence.

1. Talia plans to ____________________ the furniture in her room.
2. Due to the rainy weather we will have to ____________________ the picnic.
3. After much discussion the boys came to an ____________________.
4. Will has many choices, but he is still ____________________.
5. Good music, delicious food, and fun games made for a ____________________ party.

agreement **indecisive** **memorable** **postpone** **rearrange**

B. Write the words from the word bank below in alphabetical order.

____

____

____

____

____

meanwhile **meatball** **daydream** **playground** **download**

C. Find each word. The words go across, up and down.

newspaper
seashell
misinform
creative
impolite

E	Z	M	E	M	Y	Q	M	N	S
T	R	E	K	R	V	B	X	X	E
Z	C	E	K	O	T	F	I	C	A
C	R	U	C	F	N	U	M	V	S
N	E	F	O	N	W	N	P	N	H
L	A	Q	G	I	I	J	O	V	E
O	T	V	D	S	D	S	L	W	L
T	I	W	J	I	C	B	I	T	L
D	V	A	C	M	A	N	T	B	P
N	E	W	S	P	A	P	E	R	V

Antonyms

1

Name ______________________________

Antonyms are opposites. *Tall* and *short* are antonyms. So are *city* and *country*.

Are these words antonyms? Circle yes or no.

1. delicious	tasteless	**yes**	**no**
2. cooperative	unhelpful	**yes**	**no**
3. curious	interested	**yes**	**no**
4. thoughtful	thoughtless	**yes**	**no**
5. clever	smart	**yes**	**no**

antonyms * synonyms * homographs * homophones Week Nine
DAILY VOCABULARY PRACTICE

Antonyms

2

Name ______________________________

Antonyms are opposites. *Tall* and *short* are antonyms. So are *city* and *country*.

Read each word. Choose its antonym from the word box. Write it on the line.

1. gorgeous ______________________
2. whisper ______________________
3. flavorful ______________________
4. alert ______________________
5. victory ______________________

bland	**hideous**	**loss**	**shout**	**sleepy**

Antonyms

3

Name ______________________________

Antonyms are opposites. *Tall* and *short* are antonyms. So are *city* and *country*.

Read each group of words. Put an X on the word that is the antonym to all the others.

1. rapid	fast	slow	speedy
2. booming	silent	thunderous	loud
3. wee	immense	towering	gigantic
4. numerous	plentiful	scarce	abundant
5. tardy	late	overdue	punctual

Antonyms

Name ______________________________

Antonyms are opposites. *Tall* and *short* are antonyms. So are *city* and *country*.

Match the antonyms to make an *oxymoron*, a pair of words with a meaning that seems impossible. (Icy hot is an oxymoron.) Write each oxymoron you create on a line.

1. jumbo   again   ______________________
2. exact   news   ______________________
3. same   shrimp   ______________________
4. old   estimate   ______________________
5. never   difference   ______________________

Antonyms

5

Name ____________________________________

Antonyms are opposites. *Tall* and *short* are antonyms. So are *city* and *country*.

Choose the best word from the word box to complete each sentence. Circle the word's antonym in each sentence.

1. The store has a plain exterior, but the ________________ is quite beautiful.
2. Our flight ________________ at 5:00 p.m. and arrives at 9:30.
3. In a court of law, a person is ________________ until proven guilty.
4. The team has a good offense but they need to work on their ________________.
5. Don't ignore your ________________ as you plan for the future.

defense	**departs**	**innocent**	**interior**	**past**

Antonyms

Name ____________________________________

Read the word in the first column. Circle its antonym.

1. delicious	tasty	mouth-watering	repulsive
2. gorgeous	beautiful	plain	attractive
3. jumbo	large	immense	wee
4. depart	leave	arrive	exit
5. interior	outside	inside	innermost

DAILY VOCABULARY PRACTICE

Synonyms

1

Name ______________________________

Synonyms are words that have similar meanings.

Use an arrow to match a word on the left with its synonym on the right.

1. hard	unusual
2. bad	enormous
3. big	challenging
4. small	horrible
5. weird	miniscule

tonyms * synonyms * homographs * homophones
Week Ten

DAILY VOCABULARY PRACTICE

Synonyms

2

Name ______________________________

Synonyms are words that have similar meanings.

Read the word on the left. Find its synonym in the word box. Write the synonym on the line.

1. look ______________________

2. say ______________________

3. taste ______________________

4. hear ______________________

5. breathe ______________________

inhale	**comprehend**	**observe**	**savor**	**exclaim**

DAILY VOCABULARY PRACTICE

Synonyms

3

Name ______________________________

Synonyms are words that have similar meanings.

Put an x on the word that does not belong in the group of synonyms.

1. plentiful   sparse   abundant
2. thankful   appreciative   ungrateful
3. mean   friendly   neighborly
4. generous   stingy   benevolent
5. eat   devour   fast

antonyms ✳ synonyms ✳ homographs ✳ homophones Week Ten

DAILY VOCABULARY PRACTICE

Synonyms

Name ______________________________

Synonyms are words that have similar meanings.

Find a word that has the same meaning as the word or phrase in *italics*. Write the synonym on the line.

1. We ______________ Thanksgiving in November.
   observe
2. The first Thanksgiving ______________ in 1621.
   happened
3. Pilgrims and the Native Americans ______________ homegrown foods.
   consumed
4. Today, turkey and cranberries are a ______________ part of the Thanksgiving meal.
   customary
5. Families and friends ______________ to enjoy the feast.
   get together

traditional   celebrate   occurred   gather   ate

Synonyms

5

Name ______________________________

Synonyms are words that have similar meanings.

Unscramble the synonyms for the words on the right. Write the words on the line.

1. lolwa ______________________ permit
2. alcl ______________________ shout
3. recu ______________________ heal
4. bgra ______________________ seize
5. hirgt ______________________ correct

Synonyms

Name ______________________________

Are these words synonyms? Circle yes or no.

		Synonyms?	
1. miniskirt	miniature	**yes**	**no**
2. shout	bellow	**yes**	**no**
3. grateful	unappreciative	**yes**	**no**
4. devour	gobble	**yes**	**no**
5. observe	ignore	**yes**	**no**

DAILY VOCABULARY PRACTICE

Homographs

1

Name ______________________________

Homographs are words that are pronounced and spelled the same but have different meanings. For example, a *pitcher* is a baseball player. It is also a container for pouring drinks.

Label the picture. Match it to its homograph on the right.

1. ____________________ 

2. ____________________ 

3. ____________________ 

4. ____________________ 

5. ____________________ 

antonyms * synonyms * homographs * homophones
Week Eleven

DAILY VOCABULARY PRACTICE

Homographs

2

Name ______________________________

Homographs are words that are pronounced and spelled the same but have different meanings. For example, a *pitcher* is a baseball player. It is also a container for pouring drinks.

Match the word to its definition. Write the letter on the line.

1. hide __________
2. kind __________
3. rare __________
4. pry __________
5. stable __________

a. thoughtful; a certain type
b. a home for horses; steady
c. lightly cooked; unusual
d. animal skin; to keep out of view
e. to remove with force; to ask nosy questions

DAILY VOCABULARY PRACTICE

Homographs

3

Name ______________________________

Homographs are words that are spelled the same but have different meanings. For example, a *pitcher* is a baseball player. It is also a container for pouring drinks.

Label the pictures. Then, match the homograph. Check the word box for clues.

1. __________  __________ 

2. __________ __________

3. __________  __________ 

4. __________  __________ 

5. __________  __________ 

lock	temple	tip	squash	watch

DAILY VOCABULARY PRACTICE

Homographs

Name ______________________________

Homographs are words that are spelled the same but have different meanings. For example, a *pitcher* is a baseball player. It is also a container for pouring drinks.

Read each clue. Write the homograph that best fits both clues.

1. Part of a computer or a small rodent __________
2. A mesh-like window covering or the front of a TV set __________
3. Pieces of wood or to move in a clumsy manner __________
4. Thin sheets of metal or to mess up someone's plan __________
5. To watch carefully or a computer screen __________

foil	lumber	monitor	mouse	screen

DAILY VOCABULARY PRACTICE

Homographs

5

Name ______________________

Homographs are words that are spelled the same but have different meanings. For example, a *pitcher* is a baseball player. It is also a container for pouring drinks.

Read the clues. Write the answer on the line twice! Choose words from the word box. We've done the first one for you.

1. A bold hot dog is a frank frank.
2. A big sled dog is a ______________.
3. Part of a student's eye is a ______________.
4. A college for a group of fish is a ______________.
5. A solid business is a ______________.

firm frank husky pupil school

DAILY VOCABULARY PRACTICE

Homographs

Name ______________________

Choose the word that can be used to complete both sentences.

1. Please ______________ the papers in the box. — Lee uses a ______________ on her nails.
2. The tree ______________ is rough. — The dog's ______________ is loud.
3. The ______________ hibernates in winter. — How much weight can the bridge ______________?
4. Ed made peach ______________. — The ______________ fixed my shoes.
5. On what ______________ is your birthday? — A ______________ is a sweet and sticky fruit.

bark bear cobbler date file

Homophones

1

Name ________________________________

Homophones are words that sound the same but have different meanings. They are usually spelled differently too. *Bear* and *bare* are homophones. So are *flu* and *flew*.

Write a homophone for each word.

1. ________________________ flour
2. ________________________ close
3. ________________________ beat
4. ________________________ bough
5. ________________________ night

Homophones

2

Name ________________________________

Homophones are words that sound the same but have different meanings. They are usually spelled differently too. *Bear* and *bare* are homophones. So are *flu* and *flew*.

Choose a homophone pair to complete each sentence.

1. An up-to-date dried fruit is a ________________________.
2. A rough path is a ________________________.
3. A mammal without any fur is a ________________________.
4. Sets of sweet fruit are ________________________ of ________________________.
5. A light-colored bucket is a ________________________.

bare coarse currant bear current pail pairs course pears pale

Homophones

3

Name ______________________________

Homophones are words that sound the same but have different meanings. They are usually spelled differently too. *Bear* and *bare* are homophones. So are *flu* and *flew*.

Circle the correct homophone to complete each expression.

1. (stake, steak) your claim to the seat.
2. (waist, waste) not, want not.
3. The (whole, hole) nine yards is what the coach wants.
4. (piece, peace) on Earth, goodwill to men.
5. The (strait, straight) and narrow is the best path to follow.

antonyms ✳ synonyms ✳ homographs ✳ homophones Week Twelve

DAILY VOCABULARY PRACTICE

Homophones

4

Name ______________________________

Homophones are words that sound the same but have different meanings. They are usually spelled differently too. *Bear* and *bare* are homophones. So are *flu* and *flew*.

Circle the misspelled word in each sentence. Write a homophone on the line that would make the sentence correct.

1. You guest it! ______________________
2. Hour class is having a party. ______________________
3. Weave been planning for weeks. ______________________
4. All we knead to do now is send invitations. ______________________
5. We are looking foreword to seeing you! ______________________

© Weekly Reader Corporation

DAILY VOCABULARY PRACTICE

Homophones

5

Name ______________________________

Homophones are words that sound the same but have different meanings. They are usually spelled differently too. *Bear* and *bare* are homophones. So are *flu* and *flew*.

Read each word on the left. Write its homophone on the line.

1. allowed ______________________
2. presence ______________________
3. principal ______________________
4. capitol ______________________
5. instance ______________________

DAILY VOCABULARY PRACTICE

Homophones

Name ______________________________

Read each clue. Then, read the homophones. Circle the correct word.

Clue		
1. People who help customers	attendants	attendance
2. The foundation of something	bases	basis
3. New growth from a plant	chute	shoot
4. A sword fight	duel	dual
5. A mix of algae and fungus; grows on rocks	liken	lichen

DAILY VOCABULARY PRACTICE

Name ______________________________

A. Are these words synonyms or antonyms?

Circle one.

1. cooperative	helpful	synonym	antonym
2. gorgeous	plain	synonym	antonym
3. observe	ignore	synonym	antonym
4. devour	eat	synonym	antonym
5. challenging	easy	synonym	antonym

B. Find the homophones. Look up and down.

allowed aloud
guessed guest
peace piece

S	E	A	P	D	B
T	C	L	E	E	A
S	E	L	A	S	L
E	I	O	C	S	O
U	P	W	E	E	U
G	R	E	B	U	D
P	T	D	Z	G	G

C. Complete the puzzle.

Across

1. My synonyms are *shout*, *yell*, and *holler*.
4. I am the same as *charitable* and *giving*, and the opposite of *miserly*.
6. Use me to describe something that is steady or solid.
7. *Bold* and *straightforward* are two of my synonyms.

Down

2. I sound like presents, but I'm not a synonym for *gifts*.
3. *Loss* and *defeat* are my antonyms.
5. Use me instead of *look*, *see*, or *watch*.

presence exclaim generous observe stable victory frank

Clips

1

Name ______________________________

Clips are shortened versions of longer words.

Match the clipped word with the full word.

1. pop	telephone
2. ad	gasoline
3. doc	doctor
4. phone	popular
5. gas	advertisement

Clips

2

Name ______________________________

Clips are shortened versions of longer words.

Circle part of the word to form a clipped word. Write the clipped word on the line.

1. statistics ______________________________
2. referee ______________________________
3. gymnasium ______________________________
4. champion ______________________________
5. fanatic ______________________________

DAILY VOCABULARY PRACTICE

Clips

3

Name ____________________

Clips are shortened versions of longer words.

Fill in the missing letters to complete each word. Check the word box for clues.

1. ____ ____ ____ oratory
2. ____ ____ ____ ____ ination
3. ____ ____ ____ ____ ematics
4. ____ ____ ____ ____ itory
5. ____ ____ ____ ____ essor

exam	**lab**	**dorm**	**prof**	**math**

clips blended words new words foreign words in English Week Thirteen

DAILY VOCABULARY PRACTICE

Clips

4

Name ____________________

Clips are shortened versions of longer words.

Read each word. Find its clip on the right. Write the letter on the line.

1. automobile ____ a. sub
2. helicopter ____ b. limo
3. limousine ____ c. plane
4. submarine ____ d. copter
5. airplane ____ e. auto

Clips

5

Name ______________________________

Clips are shortened versions of longer words.

Complete each sentence. Replace the word in italics with its clipped form.

1. Patti will take a ______________ with her new camera.
   photograph
2. Tom wore a ______________ to the party.
   tuxedo
3. A person between the ages of 13 and 19 is a ______________.
   teenager
4. Lisa's sister is a ______________ of Mountain View High School.
   graduate
5. The students chose a DJ for the ______________.
   promenade

Clips

Name ______________________________

Read each clue. Write the full word and its clip on the lines.

	Full word	Clip
1. I tell you about new products. What am I?	______________	________
2. I am a place to play sports. What am I?	______________	________
3. I have to do with numbers. What am I?	______________	________
4. I fly high in the air. What am I?	______________	________
5. I am between 13 and 19 years old. What am I?	______________	________

DAILY VOCABULARY PRACTICE

Blended Words

1

Name ______________________________

Blended words combine fragments or parts of two other words to create a new word with a new meaning.

Add the two words together to form a new word. Check the word bank for clues.

1. twist + whirl = ______________________
2. wade + toddle = ______________________
3. flap + drop = ______________________
4. splash + surge = ______________________
5. twist + fiddle = ______________________

waddle	**splurge**	**twiddle**	**twirl**	**flop**

clips blended words new words foreign words in English Week Fourteen

DAILY VOCABULARY PRACTICE

Blended Words

2

Name ______________________________

Blended words combine fragments or parts of two other words to create a new word with a new meaning.

Read the clue. Write the blended word on the line.

1. I am a blend of the words *bold* and *rash*. ______________________
2. I am a blend of the words *snappy* and *jazzy*. ______________________
3. I am a blend of the words *huge* and *monstrous*. ______________________
4. I am a blend of the words *chunk* and *lump*. ______________________
5. I am a blend of the words *dizzy* and *dotty*. ______________________

snazzy	**ditsy**	**humongous**	**brash**	**chump**

DAILY VOCABULARY PRACTICE

Blended Words

3

Name ______________________________

Blended words combine fragments or parts of two other words to create a new word with a new meaning.

Match each blended word to the words it comes from.

1. blurt	*chuckle* and *snort*
2. chortle	*haggle* and *tussle*
3. hassle	*blow* and *spurt*
4. squash	*squirm* and *wriggle*
5. squiggle	*squeeze* and *crash*

DAILY VOCABULARY PRACTICE

Blended Words

4

Name ______________________________

Blended words combine fragments or parts of two other words to create a new word with a new meaning.

Read each clue. Write the word on the line. Check the word box for clues.

1. a mix between a plum and an apricot ______________
2. a meal after breakfast and before lunch ______________
3. a dried cranberry, like a raisin ______________
4. a spoon with tines, like a fork ______________
5. a mix between a tangerine and a pomelo fruit ______________

brunch	craisin	pluot	spork	tangelo

DAILY VOCABULARY PRACTICE

Blended Words

5

Name ______________________

Blended words combine fragments or parts of two other words to create a new word with a new meaning.

Complete each word equation. Check the word box for clues.

1. ______________ = boom + hoist
2. ______________ = clap + crash
3. ______________ = blank out + beep
4. ______________ = flash + gush
5. ______________ = smack + mash

bleep boost clash flush smash

clips blended words new words foreign words in English
Week Fourteen Review

DAILY VOCABULARY PRACTICE

Blended Words

Name ______________________

Read each word. Write the two words it is made of on the lines.

1. splurge ______________ + ______________
2. humongous ______________ + ______________
3. chortle ______________ + ______________
4. brunch ______________ + ______________
5. clash ______________ + ______________

breakfast	**chuckle**	**clap**	**crash**	**enormous**
huge	**lunch**	**snort**	**splash**	**surge**

DAILY VOCABULARY PRACTICE

New Words

1

Name ______________________________

Languages are constantly adding new words. For example, the word *Internet* is a new word. Before the invention of the computer, it was not part of the English language.

Match the new word on the left with the words and phrases on the right.

1. Internet	Internet etiquette
2. emoticon :-)	network between computers
3. blog	smiley
4. netiquette	electronic mail
5. e-mail	Web log

ips blended words new words foreign words in English
Week Fifteen

DAILY VOCABULARY PRACTICE

New Words

2

Name ______________________________

Languages are constantly adding new words. For example, the word *Internet* is a new word. Before the invention of the computer, it was not part of the English language.

Some new words were invented for instant messaging and text messaging. Read each phrase. Write the new word abbreviation on the line. Check the word bank for clues.

1. in my humble opinion ____________________
2. talk to you later ____________________
3. by the way ____________________
4. on the other hand ____________________
5. laughing out loud ____________________

IMHO LOL TTYL OTOH BTW

DAILY VOCABULARY PRACTICE

New Words

3

Name ______________________________

Languages are constantly adding new words. Some new words come from people's names.

Read the clues. Write the new word on the line.

1. I am a word that means, "to hypnotize." I am named after Frederich Mesmer, an Austrian hypnotist. ____________
2. I am a horn named after Anton Sax, a musical instrument maker. ____________
3. I am a stretchy piece of clothing named after the French acrobat Jules Leotard. ____________
4. I am a snack named after John Montagu, the fourth Earl of Sandwich. ____________

5. I am a shadowy image named after Etienne de Silhouette, a member of the French government and amateur artist. ____________

leotard	**mesmerize**	**sandwich**	**saxophone**	**silhouette**

clips blended words new words foreign words in English
Week Fifteen

DAILY VOCABULARY PRACTICE

New Words

Name ______________________________

Languages are constantly adding new words. For example, the word *Internet* is a new word. Before the invention of the computer, it was not part of the English language.

Fill in each blank with a word from the word bank.

1. ____________ gets its name because it takes longer to get to its destination than e-mail.
2. Unwanted e-mails from advertisers are known as ____________.
3. When you ____________ something, you are using the Internet search engine to do research.
4. An online journal, or Web log, is called a ____________.
5. A person who keeps an online journal, or blog, is called a ____________.

blog	**blogger**	**Google**	**snail mail**	**spam**

5

New Words

Name ______________________________

Some new words are acronyms, made by putting together letters from the words that make it up.

Read each clue. Write the new word on the line. Check the word bank for clues.

1. *ra*dio *d*etecting *a*nd *r*anging ______________
2. *l*ight *a*mplification by *s*imulated *e*mission of *r*adiation ______________
3. *s*elf *c*ontained *u*nderwater *b*reathing *a*pparatus ______________
4. *so*und *na*vigation *r*anging ______________

radar	**laser**	**scuba**	**sonar**

New Words

Name ______________________________

On the line, write the word that best fits the description.

1. a blend of the word *network* and the prefix meaning *"between"* ______________
2. used in text messaging to say "by the way" ______________
3. named after Frederich Mesmer; a synonym of the word *hypnotize*. ______________
4. an online journal; a blend of the words *Web* and *log* ______________
5. the L in this word stands for *light.* ______________

mesmerize	**laser**	**Internet**	**BTW**	**blog**

DAILY VOCABULARY PRACTICE

Foreign Words in English

1

Name ______________________________

Many English words are based on words from other languages.

Latin is an ancient language. English words are often based on Latin words. Read each clue. Write the answer on the line.

1. I come from the Latin root *form* (shape). ____________________
2. I come from the Latin root *clamare* (shout). ____________________
3. I come from the Latin root *spec* (to see). ____________________
4. I come from the Latin root *vac* (empty). ____________________
5. I come from the Latin root *rupt* (break). ____________________

exclaim interrupt spectator evacuate transform

clips blended words new words foreign words in English Week Sixteen

DAILY VOCABULARY PRACTICE

Foreign Words in English

2

Name ______________________________

Many words in the English language are formed from Greek words, or a combination of Greek and Latin words. Read each clue. Write the new word on the line.

1. *manu* (hand) + *fac* (make, or do) = ____________________ (to make by hand)
2. *bio* (life) + *graph* (write) = ____________________ (a book written about someone's life)
3. *therm* (heat) + *meter* (measure) = ____________________ (a tool used to measure temperature)
4. *cosmo* (universe) + *poli* (city) = ____________________ (a word used to describe a large city)
5. *manu* (hand) + *script* (write) = ____________________ (written by hand)

manuscript manufacture cosmopolitan thermometer biography

DAILY VOCABULARY PRACTICE

Foreign Words in English

3

Name ____________________________

These words come from characters in Greek and Roman myths. Read each clue. Write the answer on the line. Check the word box for clues.

1. from Ceres (Roman), goddess of agriculture ____________________
2. from Electra (Greek), daughter of Agamemnon ____________________
3. from Vulcan (Roman), the god of fire ____________________
4. from the Amazons (Greek), women warriors ____________________
5. from Hygeia (Greek), goddess of health ____________________

amazonian	cereal	electricity	hygiene	volcano

DAILY VOCABULARY PRACTICE

Foreign Words in English

Name ____________________________

Read the definition. Write the answer on the line.
Check the word box to see the country or region that it comes from.

1. a fruit that is peeled before it's eaten ____________________
2. a vegetable with spiky leaves ____________________
3. a food made from soybeans ____________________
4. a sweet biscuit ____________________
5. a type of meat used to make sandwiches ____________________

Africa	Holland	Italy	China	Arabia
banana	cookie	bologna	tofu	artichoke

DAILY VOCABULARY PRACTICE

Foreign Words in English

5

Name ______________________

Many English words are based on words from other languages.

Read each word and its definition. Match each word to its place of origin.

1. cashmere, a soft wool	Cologne, Germany
2. cologne, a perfume	Mosul, Iraq
3. manila, a kind of paper	Tangiers, Morocco
4. tangerine, a citrus fruit	Kashmir, India
5. muslin, a fabric	Manila, Philippines

DAILY VOCABULARY PRACTICE

Foreign Words in English

Name ______________________

Complete each sentence. Check the word box for clues.

1. During the fire drill we had to ______________________.
2. The doctor used a ______________________ to take the boy's temperature.
3. The bright lights are powered by ______________________.
4. The child ate a ______________________ sandwich for lunch.
5. A ______________________ looks like a small orange.

bologna	**electricity**	**evacuate**	**tangerine**	**thermometer**

Monthly Review 4

DAILY VOCABULARY PRACTICE

Name ______________________________

A. Choose the best word to complete each sentence.

1. Scarlet is a huge basketball ____________________; she doesn't miss a single game.
2. Lin took lots of ____________________ on her family vacation.
3. The gymnast wore a black ____________________.
4. Devon writes a ____________________ about BMX bikes.
5. A ____________________ shoots a beam of light.

blog	**fan**	**laser**	**leotard**	**photos**

B. Choose a word from Group 1 and a word from Group 2 to form a new word.

		Group 1	**Group 2**
1. __________ + __________	= clash	splash	surge
2. __________ + __________	= splurge	huge	lunch
3. __________ + __________	= brunch	squirm	wriggle
4. __________ + __________	= humongous	breakfast	monstrous
5. __________ + __________	= squiggle	clap	crash

C. Find each word. The words go up and down, backwards, and diagonally.

brash
spam
transform
phone
mesmerize
spectator

E	Z	J	J	P	B	M	F	F	S
N	Z	Z	U	H	E	Z	K	P	P
O	V	I	J	O	Z	Y	E	K	T
H	J	S	R	N	X	C	T	H	V
P	K	E	N	E	T	Y	B	L	B
L	F	S	P	A	M	Z	U	S	P
X	G	T	T	M	H	S	A	R	B
O	P	O	Y	H	A	Q	E	U	F
T	R	A	N	S	F	O	R	M	C

DAILY VOCABULARY PRACTICE

Science Words

1

Name ______________________________

Environmental words describe the world around us and the natural things in it.

Unscramble each word. Check your answers in the word box. Write each word on the line.

1. oncae, a large body of water ____________________
2. reedts, very dry land ____________________
3. ortesf, an area with many trees ____________________
4. aadgslrsn, a prairie ____________________
5. eatlndw, a marsh or swamp ____________________

desert	**forest**	**ocean**	**grassland**	**wetland**

DAILY VOCABULARY PRACTICE

Science Words

2

Name ______________________________

Environmental words describe the world around us and the natural elements in it.

Read the clues. Write the best answer on the line.

1. I am a winter storm. I snow for three hours or more. ____________________
2. I start as a funnel cloud. I can pull trees from the ground. ____________________
3. I am a very strong storm. In Japan I am a typhoon. Australians call me a Willy-Willy.

   ____
4. I am very dry. I can cause water shortages and destroy crops. ____________________
5. I am a storm with bright lights and booming sounds. ____________________

drought	**thunderstorm**	**hurricane**	**tornado**	**blizzard**

DAILY VOCABULARY PRACTICE

Science Words

3

Name ______________________________

Environmental words describe the world around us and the natural elements in it.

Complete the words by filling in the missing vowels.

1. Cl____m____t____ is the weather in a particular place over time.
2. ____tm____sph____r____ is a layer of gases surrounding the Earth.
3. T____mp____r____t____r____ is a measurement of heat.
4. ____z____n____ is a gas.
5. W____ ____ th____r is the temperature and precipitation at a particular time.

environmental words animals science words space words
Week Seventeen

DAILY VOCABULARY PRACTICE

Science Words

Name ______________________________

Environmental words describe the world around us and the natural elements in it.

Use what you know to complete each sentence.

1. A thermometer is used to measure ______________________.
2. Temperature is measured in ______________________.
3. In the United States, temperature is measured on the ______________________ scale.
4. Thirty-two degrees Fahrenheit is the same as zero degrees on the ______________________ scale that most of the world uses.
5. A ______________________ is an instrument used to measure air pressure.

barometer **Celsius** **degrees** **Fahrenheit** **temperature**

DAILY VOCABULARY PRACTICE

Science Words

5

Name ________________________________

Environmental words describe the world around us and the natural elements in it.

Match each word to its definition.

1. environment	the study of the natural environment
2. habitat	dirtying of the soil, air or water
3. pollution	the home territory of a living thing
4. litter	the natural world
5. ecology	trash

DAILY VOCABULARY PRACTICE

Science Words

Name ________________________________

Add the vowels to complete each word. Match each word to its definition.

1. gr___ssl___nd	a measure of how hot or cold something is
2. dr___ ___ght	the slow wearing away of the earth and rock
3. cl___m___t___	a period without rain; can damage crops
4. t___mp___r___t___r___	an area covered with grass, without trees or shrubs
5. ___r___s___ ___n	typical weather conditions in a region

Science Words

1

Name ________________________________

Most animal forms are divided into two groups, vertebrates and invertebrates. Vertebrates have a backbone; invertebrates do not.

Circle the correct answer.

1. A vertebrate has a backbone. **True** **False**
2. An invertebrate has a backbone. **True** **False**
3. Humans are invertebrates. **True** **False**
4. A fly is an invertebrate. **True** **False**
5. Most of the world's animals are invertebrates. **True** **False**

vironmental words animals science words space words
Week Eighteen
DAILY VOCABULARY PRACTICE

Science Words

2

Name ________________________________

Animals can also be grouped by what they eat; herbivores eat only plants, carnivores eat only other animals, and omnivores eat anything.

Is it an herbivore, carnivore or omnivore? Fill in the blank after each sentence with the correct label.

1. Cows eat a simple diet of grasses. ______________________
2. A cheetah chases other animals of the African plains to eat them.

   ____
3. My dog eats a mix of canned meat and grains. ______________________
4. The birds pecked at seeds and wild blueberries. ______________________
5. The pigs ate whatever they found in the garbage. ______________________

DAILY VOCABULARY PRACTICE

Science Words

3

Name ______________________________

Use what you know. Label each picture with the correct word from the word bank.

1. ______________________ 

2. ______________________ 

3. ______________________ 

4. ______________________ 

5. ______________________ 

amphibian mammal insect bird reptile

environmental words animals science words space words Week Eighteen

DAILY VOCABULARY PRACTICE

Science Words

4

Name ______________________________

Some animals go through a cycle of changes from one life form to another.

Circle the best word to complete each sentence. Read all the sentences before you begin.

1. Like many insects, a Monarch butterfly starts out as an (egg/chrysalis).
2. The egg hatches and a (worm/caterpillar) emerges.
3. After eating for a few weeks, the caterpillar forms a (chrysalis/egg) around itself.
4. Finally, a (caterpillar/butterfly) comes out of the chrysalis.
5. This process is called the (spin cycle/life cycle).

DAILY VOCABULARY PRACTICE

Science Words

5

Name ______________________________

Circle the word that is spelled incorrectly. Write the correct spelling on the line.

1. Whales live in an ocean habbutat. ____________
2. In the winter, many animals mygreat to warm climates. ____________
3. Some animals cammoflaj themselves to blend into their environment. ____________
4. Bears hybernayt in the winter. ____________
5. People can help to protect indanjered animals. ____________

habitat	**endangered**	**migrate**	**camouflage**	**hibernate**

DAILY VOCABULARY PRACTICE

Science Words

Name ______________________________

Circle the best word to complete each sentence.

1. Animals with backbones are called **vertebrates/invertebrates**.
2. A meat-eating animal is known as a(n) **herbivore/carnivore**.
3. Human beings and furry animals are **mammals/amphibians**.
4. Animals **endanger/camouflage** themselves to blend in with the environment.
5. The **chrysalis/life cycle** is a series of stages in an animal's development.

DAILY VOCABULARY PRACTICE

Science Words

1

Name ______________________________

Complete each sentence. Check the word bank for clues.

1. I am a muscle. As I beat, I move blood through the body.
   I am the ____________________.
2. I am a sac that mashes food and partly digests it.
   I am your ____________________.
3. There are more than 200 of me. We support your body.
   We are ____________________.
4. I am your control center. I am your ____________________.

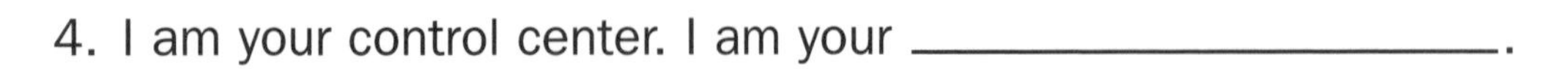

5. By pushing and pulling, I help move bones and body parts.

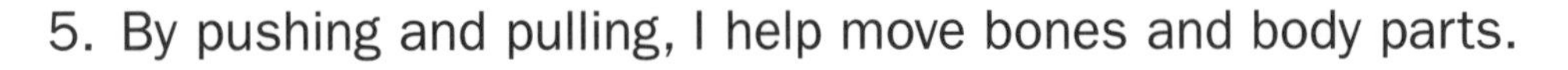

   I am your ____________________.

bones	brain	heart	muscles	stomach

environmental words · animals · science words · space words
Week Nineteen

DAILY VOCABULARY PRACTICE

Science Words

2

Name ______________________________

Match each word to its description.

1. enamel — a way to clean between teeth
2. floss — the hardest substance in the human body; the surface of the tooth
3. cavity — the first thing you do to clean your teeth
4. brush — they keep your teeth secure
5. gums — a diseased tooth has one

Science Words

3

Name ____________________

Complete each sentence. Check the word box for clues.

1. A balanced diet is important for good ____________.
2. Meat, fish, and tofu are good sources of ____________.
3. Bread, rice, and cereal are ____________.
4. Mangoes, tomatoes, and bok choy are good sources of ____________ A and C.
5. Eating the right foods every day gives the body ____________ and strength.

vitamins	**energy**	**protein**	**grains**	**nutrition**

vironmental words animals science words space words Week Nineteen
DAILY VOCABULARY PRACTICE

Science Words

4

Name ____________________

Choose the best word to complete each sentence.

1. It's a good idea to see a doctor for a ____________ once a year.
2. The doctor can make sure your ____________ are up to date.
3. You may read an eye chart to check your ____________.
4. The doctor may listen to your heart and lungs with a ____________.
5. The doctor will look into your ears, nose and ____________.

check-up	**stethoscope**	**throat**	**vaccinations**	**vision**

DAILY VOCABULARY PRACTICE

Science Words

5

Name ______________________________

Read the clue. Write the answer on the line.

1. Another word for illness is ________________.
2. A person who has a disease that can be passed to another person is ________________.
3. A disease or health condition that does not go away is ________________.
4. A microbe, or ________________, can cause disease.
5. A sign of disease is called a ________________.

chronic	contagious	disease	germ	symptom

DAILY VOCABULARY PRACTICE

Science Words

Name ______________________________

Unscramble each word. Write it on the line. Use the definitions for clues.

1. nleema	________________	the surface of a tooth
2. iontrintu	________________	healthy eating
3. merg	________________	microbe
4. usclesm	________________	they move your bones
5. copestethos	________________	a doctor’s listening tool

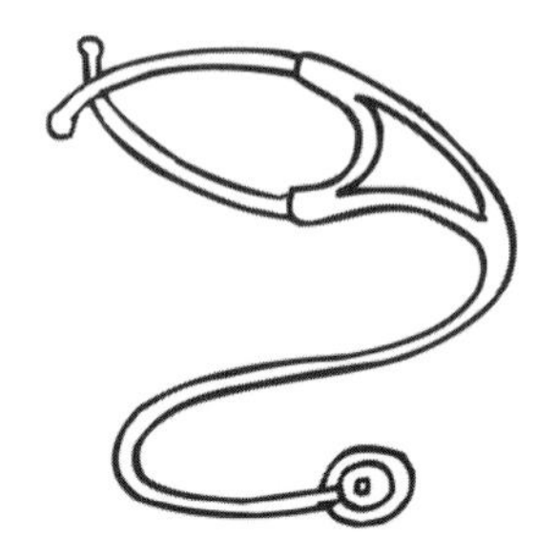

DAILY VOCABULARY PRACTICE

Science Words

1

Name ___________________________

The study of space science helps us to better understand the world in which we live.

Read each clue. Write the correct answer on the line.

1. I am surrounded by rings. _______________
2. I am about the same size as Earth. _______________
3. I am the farthest planet from the sun. _______________
4. I am the third planet from the sun. _______________
5. I am the planet closest to the sun. _______________

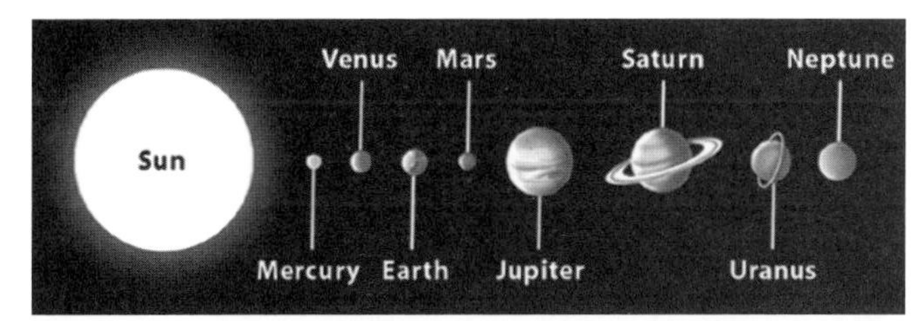

DAILY VOCABULARY PRACTICE

Science Words

2

Name ___________________________

The study of space science helps us to better understand the world in which we live.

Complete each sentence.

1. The sun is the center of the _______________ system.
2. The _______________ is the largest object in the solar system.
3. All planets _______________ the sun.
4. There are eight _______________ in the solar system.
5. Our solar system is part of the _______________.

Milky Way   orbit   planets   solar   sun

DAILY VOCABULARY PRACTICE

Science Words

3

Name ______________________________

The study of space science helps us to better understand the world in which we live.

Fill in the missing vowels to label each picture.

1. st____r
2. pl____n____t
3. c____m____t
4. m____t____ ____r
5. m____ ____n

environmental words animals science words space words Week Twenty

DAILY VOCABULARY PRACTICE

Science Words

Name ______________________________

The study of space science helps us to better understand the world in which we live.

Proofread each sentence. Circle the word that is spelled incorrectly. Write the correct spelling on the line.

1. The astronot went on a space mission. ____________________
2. The Milky Way is a galacsy. ____________________
3. A galaxy is held together by gravitee. ____________________
4. Astronomers say that the unavers is very old. ____________________
5. NASA is in charge of U.S. spays exploration. ____________________

DAILY VOCABULARY PRACTICE

Science Words

5

Name ________________________________

The study of space science helps us to better understand the world in which we live.

Match the word to its definition.

1. observatory	a. the study of objects in space
2. constellation	b. a tool used to see into space
3. astronomy	c. an observation center
4. telescope	d. a scientist who studies objects in space
5. astronomer	e. a group of stars

DAILY VOCABULARY PRACTICE

Science Words

Name ________________________________

Read each clue. Write the correct answer on the line.

1. I am the third planet from the sun and home to humans. ______________
2. I am an adjective that refers to the sun. ______________
3. I am one of many small, rocky bodies in the solar system. ______________
4. My name is often used to describe the opposite of weightlessness in space. ______________
5. I am a group of stars that forms a pattern in the sky. ______________

asteroid	constellation	Earth	gravity	solar

DAILY VOCABULARY PRACTICE

Name ______________________________

A. Sort the words into two categories.

Space Science	Earth Science
______________	______________
______________	______________
______________	______________

astronomy asteroid climate constellation drought erosion

B. Write the words below in alphabetical order from top to bottom.

_ _ ☐ _ _ _ _

_ _ _ _ ☐ _ _ _ _ _ _ _

_ _ _ _ _ ☐ _ _

_ _ ☐ _ _

_ _ _ _ ☐ _ _ _ _ _ _ _

I rhyme with humor.
I am spread by gossips.

____

invertebrate communicable chronic consumer floss

C. Complete the puzzle.

Across

1. Polar bears live in the Arctic __________.
6. Eat a variety of foods for good __________.

Down

2. The wildlife park is meant to look like the animal's natural __________.
3. Is the bear a __________? Does it eat meat?
4. __________ are found in rocks *and* in food.
5. Ali lives in a cool __________; it snows in the winter.

carnivore climate habitat minerals nutrition tundra

DAILY VOCABULARY PRACTICE

Math Words

1

Name ______________________________

Write the math word that describes the operation on the line.

1. 26 – 22 ______________________
2. 201 x 23 ______________________
3. 1/23 ______________________
4. 48 + 96 ______________________
5. $45\overline{)556}$ ______________________

DAILY VOCABULARY PRACTICE

Math Words

2

Name ______________________________

Read each group of words. Place an x on the word that does not belong.

1. answer	solution	problem
2. same	different	equivalent
3. letter	numeral	number
4. combine	add	remove
5. estimate	round	exact

DAILY VOCABULARY PRACTICE

Math Words

3

Name ______________________

Read the clue. Write the answer on the line.

1. I have more than one digit. What kind of number am I? ____________
2. I am a number with only two factors. What kind of number am I? ____________
3. I cannot be divided evenly by two. What kind of number am I? ____________
4. I can be divided evenly by two. What kind of number am I? ____________
5. I have a minus sign. What kind of number am I? ____________

even odd prime multi-digit negative

DAILY VOCABULARY PRACTICE

Math Words

4

Name ______________________

Read each clue. Write the correct math verb on the line.

1. to change ____________
2. to figure out ____________
3. to reduce ____________
4. to add ____________
5. to lengthen ____________

convert extend determine increase decrease

Math Words

5

Name ______________________________

Complete each sentence using a word from the word box.

1. What is your ________________ for adding big numbers?
2. One strategy is to ________________ your answer.
3. This is a good strategy if you don't have time to make the actual ________________.
4. By estimating you will get an ________________ answer, but it won't be exact.
5. When you are done you should check to see if your estimate is ________________.

approximate strategy reasonable computation estimate

Math Words

Name ______________________________

Choose the best word to complete each sentence.

1. 8 x 5 is an example of ________________.
2. If two sums are ________________, it means they are of equal value.
3. A ________________ number is a number that is less than zero.
4. A ________________ is a way of figuring out a problem.
5. When numbers get larger, they ________________ in value.

equivalent increase multiplication negative strategy

DAILY VOCABULARY PRACTICE

Math Words

1

Name ______________________________

Geometry is the study of shapes.

Draw a line from the shape to its name.

1. hexagon
2. octagon
3. triangle
4. rectangle
5. circle

Week Twenty-Two

DAILY VOCABULARY PRACTICE

Math Words

2

Name ______________________________

Geometry is the study of shapes.

Look at each shape. Write its name on the line.

1. ______________________
2. ______________________
3. 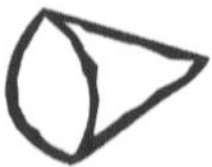 ______________________
4.  ______________________
5.  ______________________

cone cube cylinder pyramid sphere

Math Words

3

Name ______________________________

Geometry is the study of shapes.

Read each clue. Write the correct answer on the line.

1. I have three sides. I am a ______________________.
2. I have four sides. I am a ______________________.
3. I have four equal sides. I am a ______________________.
4. I have five sides. I am an ______________________.
5. I have six sides. I am a ______________________.

hexagon	**pentagon**	**rectangle**	**square**	**triangle**

eometry math words measurement percentages and fractions
Week Twenty-Two
DAILY VOCABULARY PRACTICE

Math Words

4

Name ______________________________

Geometry is the study of shapes. Polygons are shapes with more than one side.

Circle the correct answer for each word clue.

1. I am a polygon with three sides.	triangle	pentagon
2. I am a polygon with four sides.	pentagon	quadrilateral
3. I am a polygon with five sides.	octagon	pentagon
4. I am a polygon with six sides.	hexagon	pentagon
5. I am a polygon with eight sides.	quadrilateral	octagon

DAILY VOCABULARY PRACTICE

Math Words

5

Name ______________________________

Geometry is the study of shapes.

Complete each sentence using a word from the word box.

1. Two lines that never cross are called ______________ lines.
2. The perimeter of an object is the ______________ around it.
3. A ______________ has no parallel lines.
4. Diameter is measured from side to side through the ______________ of a circle.
5. Get the area of a rectangle by multiplying its length by its ______________.

center	**circle**	**distance**	**parallel**	**width**

DAILY VOCABULARY PRACTICE

Math Words

Name ______________________________

Label each picture.

1. 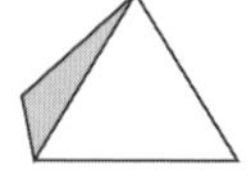 
2.  
3. 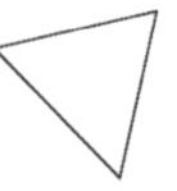 
4. 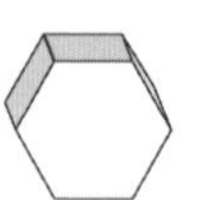 ______________
5. ______________

cylinder	**hexagon**	**parallel lines**	**pyramid**	**triangle**

DAILY VOCABULARY PRACTICE

Math Words

1

Name ________________________________

Different words and phrases are used to describe weights and measures.

Match the measurement word with its abbreviation.

1. inch	lb.
2. foot	oz.
3. ounce	in.
4. mile	ft.
5. pound	mi.

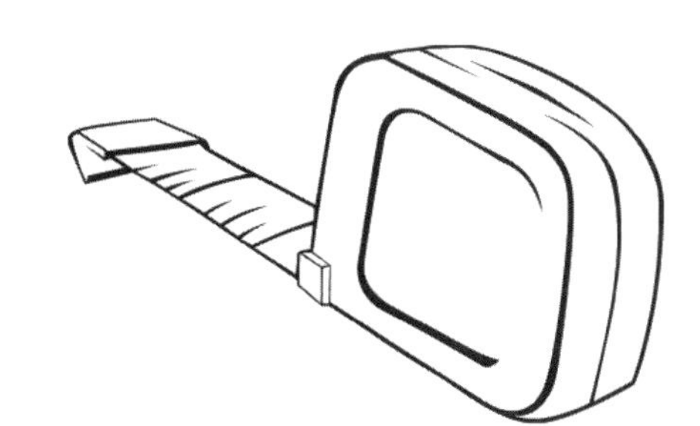

DAILY VOCABULARY PRACTICE

Math Words

2

Name ________________________________

Different words and phrases are used to describe weights and measures.

Complete each sentence. Use the word box for clues.

1. Eight fluid ounces equals one ________________.
2. Two cups equals one ________________.
3. Sixteen fluid ________________ equals one pint.
4. Two pints equals one ________________.
5. Four quarts equals one ________________.

cup gallon ounces pint quart

Math Words

3

Name ______________________________

Different words and phrases are used to describe weights and measures.

Write the best answer on the line. What tool would you use…

1. to check the temperature? ____________________
2. to weigh a bag of apples? ____________________
3. to measure the length of a room? ____________________
4. to measure a sheet of paper in inches? ____________________
5. to measure ten centimeters? ____________________

tape measure	**customary ruler**	**thermometer**	**metric ruler**	**scale**

Math Words

4

Name ______________________________

Different words and phrases are used to describe weights and measures.

Write the letter of the related word or term on the line.

__________	1. pounds and ounces	a. liquid capacity
__________	2. inches and feet	b. area
__________	3. fluid ounces	c. weight
__________	4. square inches and square feet	d. volume
__________	5. cubic inches and cubic feet	e. length

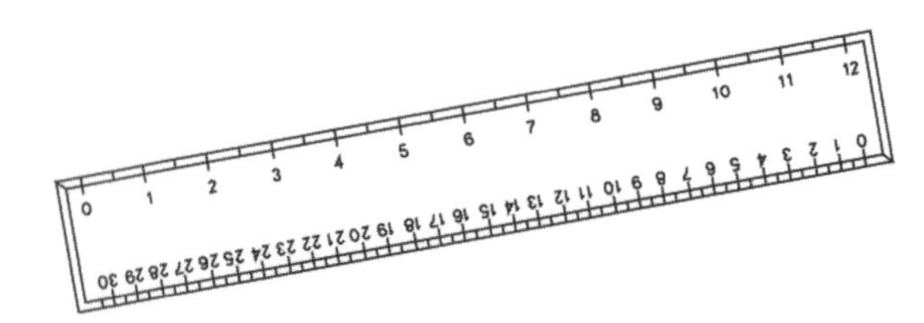

Week Twenty-Three

Math Words

Name ______________________________

Different words and phrases are used to describe weights and measures.

Put an X on the word that does not belong in each group.

1. centimeter   mile   kilometer
2. gram   milligram   pound
3. cup   liter   milliliter
4. quart   gallon   liter
5. pound   ounce   gram

Week Twenty-Three Review

Math Words

Name ______________________________

Circle the best answer.

1. Human weight is measured in what?   pounds   feet   gallons
2. What tool measures length in centimeters?   cup   scale   metric ruler
3. A small bag of spices is best measured in what?   tons   ounces   quarts
4. What unit of measure is used in most foot races?   centimeter   meter   liter
5. Cubic inches and feet are used to measured what?   weight   volume   height

DAILY VOCABULARY PRACTICE

Math Words

1

Name ____________________

Choose the best word to complete each sentence.

1. A ____________ is written as two numbers separated by a line.
2. The top number of a fraction is called the ____________.
3. The bottom number is called the ____________.
4. To add two fractions, they must have a ____________ denominator.
5. To add fractions that have unlike denominators, you can ____________ the fraction.

denominator common simplify fraction numerator

Week Twenty-Four

DAILY VOCABULARY PRACTICE

Math Words

2

Name ____________________

Choose the best label for the shaded part of each picture.

1. ____________

2. 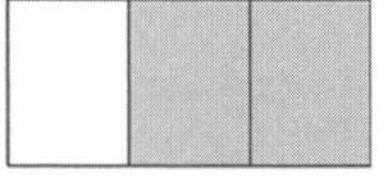 ____________

3. 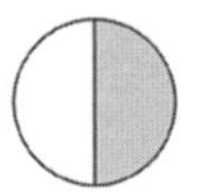 ____________

4. 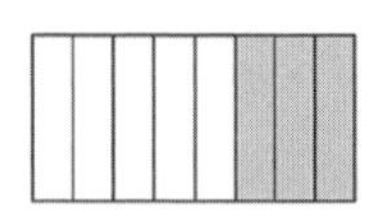 ____________

5. 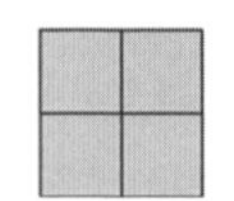 ____________

half two-thirds whole quarter three-eighths

DAILY VOCABULARY PRACTICE

Math Words

3

Name ______________________________

Fill in each blank with a word from the word box that matches the definition.

1. ______________ fractions that are equal
2. ______________ to change
3. ______________ a fraction with a numerator larger than the denominator
4. ______________ a fraction with the denominator larger than the numerator
5. ______________ a number that cannot be divided except by itself or the number one.

convert equivalent improper fraction prime proper fraction

DAILY VOCABULARY PRACTICE

Math Words

4

Name ______________________________

Circle the best answer.

1. A fraction can be converted, or changed, into a **decimal/sum.**
2. The decimal 0.5 can be pronounced as zero **period/point** five.
3. The number 2.75 has two **numbers/digits** after the decimal point.
4. You can **square/round** the decimal 5.829 to the nearest tenth.
5. In the number 7.18499 each digit has a different place **location/value.**

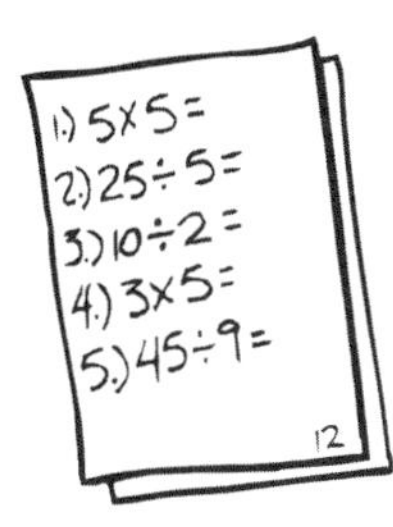

DAILY VOCABULARY PRACTICE

Math Words

5

Name ______________________________

Look at the number 8.60243

1. The 6 is in the ______________________ place.
2. The 2 is in the ______________________ place.
3. The 3 is in the ______________________ place.
4. The 4 is in the ______________________ place.
5. The 0 is in the ______________________ place.

tenths	hundredths	thousandths	ten thousandths	hundred thousandths

DAILY VOCABULARY PRACTICE

Math Words

Name ______________________________

Unscramble each word. Use the clues and the word bank. Write each word on a line.

1. pisifmyl (make easier) ______________
2. ohlew (entire) ______________
3. entocrv (change) ______________
4. idigt (0 to 9) ______________
5. htnsudotahs (a place) ______________

Monthly Review 6

DAILY VOCABULARY PRACTICE

Name ______________________________

A. Choose the best word to complete each sentence.

1. One half and two-fourths are ______________ fractions.
2. The top number in a fraction is called the ______________.
3. The ______________ is the number on the bottom of a fraction.
4. An improper fraction can be ______________, or changed, into a proper fraction.
5. A fraction can be converted into a ______________.

converted equivalent decimal denominator numerator

B. Sort the words into two categories.

Geometry Words	Measurement Words
______________	______________
______________	______________
______________	______________

cylinder kilometer line mile ounce rectangle

C. Find each word. The words go across and down, backwards, and diagonally.

strategy
simplify
prime
estimate
negative
extend
geometry

T	A	E	M	M	I	T	S	E	Q
U	R	N	E	G	A	T	I	V	E
E	O	P	X	P	R	I	M	E	S
O	Q	T	P	A	A	O	P	O	T
P	E	X	T	E	N	D	L	T	I
T	M	E	S	A	O	C	I	Y	M
D	G	W	O	A	N	E	F	S	A
Y	F	Z	R	P	F	Z	Y	Y	T
G	E	O	M	E	T	R	Y	E	E
R	Z	C	K	I	E	V	V	X	T

Geography Words

1

Name ________________________________

Maps and globes help us learn about our world.

Match the word with its definition.

1. a plan of an area	geography
2. a mapmaker	globe
3. a round model of the Earth	map
4. a book of maps	cartographer
5. the study of the earth	atlas

geography words
DAILY VOCABULARY PRACTICE
Week Twenty-Five

Geography Words

2

Name ________________________________

Maps and globes help us learn about our world.

Complete each sentence with an answer from the word bank.

1. The world is divided into a northern and a southern ____________________.
2. The ____________________ divides the northern and southern hemispheres.
3. Latitude and ____________________ lines are used to locate places on maps and globes.
4. Lines of ____________________ run parallel to the equator.
5. Lines of longitude run from the North to the South ____________________.

equator hemisphere latitude longitude pole

DAILY VOCABULARY PRACTICE

Geography Words

3

Name ______________________________

Maps and globes help us learn about our world.

Write the letter of the word that names the type of map you would use on the line.

_______ 1. I show the boundaries between countries.

_______ 2. I show landforms such as mountains and rivers.

_______ 3. I show a region's natural resources.

_______ 4. I show highways, roads, and airports.

_______ 5. I show how hot or cold an area is.

A. road map

B. climate map

C. political map

D. resource map

E. physical map

geography words geography words
Week Twenty-Five

DAILY VOCABULARY PRACTICE

Geography Words

4

Name ______________________________

Maps and globes help us learn about our world.

Circle the correct word to complete each sentence.

1. A **compass rose/key** is used to show directions on a map.
2. Maps are drawn to **exact measurements/scale.**
3. A star is a **legend/symbol** used on a map to mark state capitals.
4. Political maps show the **borders/compass rose** between countries.
5. To understand the symbols on a map, read the map **story/key.**

DAILY VOCABULARY PRACTICE

Geography Words

5

Name ______________________________

Unscramble the words. Each names one of the Earth's five oceans. Write the words on the line.

1. taAnclti ____________________
2. cfcPaii ____________________
3. ainndl ____________________
4. crActi ____________________
5. outhSern ____________________

DAILY VOCABULARY PRACTICE

Geography Words

Name ______________________________

Read each clue. Write the best answer on the line.

1. I am a person who makes maps. ____________________
2. My name means "half of a sphere." ____________________
3. I show borders, or boundaries, between countries. ____________________
4. I show directions on a map. ____________________
5. I am one of three oceans bordering the U.S. ____________________

Atlantic   cartographer   compass rose   hemisphere   political map

© Weekly Reader Corporation

DAILY VOCABULARY PRACTICE

Geography Words

Name ______________________________

There are four main points on a compass. The points are labeled N, E, S, and W. Look at the compass. Complete the sentences.

1. The top of the compass is labeled N.
   N stands for ____________________.

2. The bottom of the compass is labeled S.
   S stands for ____________________.

3. The right of the compass is labeled E.
   E stands for ____________________.

4. The left of the compass is labeled W.
   W stands for ____________________.

5. Circle one: N, E, S, and W are cardinal/intermediate directions.

geography words geography words Week Twenty-Six

DAILY VOCABULARY PRACTICE

Geography Words

2

Name ______________________________

Match each word with its abbreviation.

1. Northwest	NE
2. Southeast	SW
3. Northeast	SE
4. Southwest	NW

5. Circle one: NW, SE, NE, and SW are cardinal/intermediate directions.

DAILY VOCABULARY PRACTICE

Geography Words

3

Name ______________________________

The U.S. has five regions, or parts. Look at the map. Match each state to the region to which it belongs.

_______	1. California	a. Northeast
_______	2. Florida	b. Southwest
_______	3. Massachusetts	c. Far West
_______	4. New Mexico	d. Southeast
_______	5. Iowa	e. Midwest

geography words geography words
Week Twenty-Six

DAILY VOCABULARY PRACTICE

Geography Words

4

Name ______________________________

Five states have directions in their names. Circle the correct name for each state.

1. North Carolina	or	East Carolina
2. South Virginia	or	West Virginia
3. North Dakota	or	West Dakota
4. East Dakota	or	South Dakota
5. West Carolina	or	South Carolina

DAILY VOCABULARY PRACTICE

Geography Words

5

Name ______________________________

Use the word *north* or *south* to complete each sentence.

1. The ______________ Pole is located north of the equator.
2. The South Pole is located ______________ of the equator.
3. ______________ America is located in the western hemisphere, above the equator.
4. ______________ America is mostly located in the southern hemisphere.
5. ______________ Africa is a country in Africa.

DAILY VOCABULARY PRACTICE

Geography Words

Name ______________________________

Match the abbreviation with the full word.

1. N	Southwest
2. NE	Northwest
3. SW	South
4. S	Northeast
5. NW	North

Label the compass rose with the following directions: N, S, E, W. NE, NW, SE, SW

DAILY VOCABULARY PRACTICE

Geography Words

1

Name ______________________

The Earth's surface is made up of many different landforms.

Put an X on the word that does not belong in each group.

1. hill	mountain	swamp
2. ocean	lake	mountain
3. geyser	cave	waterfall
4. cove	hill	bay
5. glacier	spring	stream

geography words geography words Week Twenty-Seven

DAILY VOCABULARY PRACTICE

Geography Words

2

Name ______________________

The Earth's surface is made up of many different landforms.

Unscramble the words. (Each names a continent.)

1. cfAiar ______________________
2. eoruEp ______________________
3. siaA ______________________
4. laceanO ______________________
5. atcArtnic ______________________

Extra! Name two more continents:

____

DAILY VOCABULARY PRACTICE

Geography Words

3

Name ______________________________

The Earth's surface is made of many different landforms.

Read each clue. Write the best answer on the line.

1. I start with the letter M. I am a very tall landform. What am I? ______________
2. I am an area of land that gets very little water. What am I? ______________
3. I am a wide area of flat, high land. What am I? ______________
4. I am low land between two mountains or hills. What am I? ______________
5. I am a deep valley with steep sides. What am I? ______________

canyon	**desert**	**mountain**	**plateau**	**valley**

eography words geography words
Week Twenty-Seven

DAILY VOCABULARY PRACTICE

Geography Words

4

Name ______________________________

The Earth's surface is made of many different landforms.

Read the definition and fill in the missing vowels.

1. c___ ___st — land located along the ocean
2. d___lt___ — triangle of land where a river flows into the sea
3. c___p___ — a piece of land that juts out into the ocean
4. g___lf — a large area of ocean that is partially surrounded by land
5. c___v___ — a small inlet

DAILY VOCABULARY PRACTICE

Geography Words

5

Name ______________________________

The Earth's surface is made of many different landforms.

Read each definition. Circle the best answer.

1. land surrounded by water on all sides	island	or	peninsula
2. a group of islands	cape	or	archipelago
3. land with water on three sides only	island	or	peninsula
4. a narrow strip of land with water on two sides	island	or	isthmus
5. a ring-like small coral island	isthmus	or	atoll

DAILY VOCABULARY PRACTICE

Geography Words

Name ______________________________

Match each word with its definition.

1. plateau	triangle of land where a river flows into the sea
2. Europe	an area of land that is flat and high
3. canyon	one of the seven continents on Earth
4. delta	a group of small islands
5. archipelago	a deep valley with steep sides

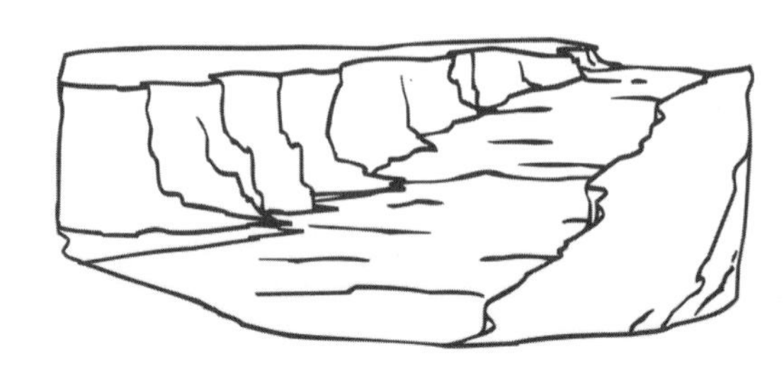

DAILY VOCABULARY PRACTICE

Geography Words

1

Name ______________________________

Add the missing vowels to complete each word.

1. w___v___s — the up and down movement of water
2. w___nd — the movement of air
3. w___t___r — It covers 7/10 of the earth's surface.
4. ___c___ — It covers most of Antarctica.
5. s___rf___c___ — Erosion caused by waves, wind, water, and ice changes the Earth's ______________.

DAILY VOCABULARY PRACTICE

Geography Words

2

Name ______________________________

Label the volcano. Use the definitions below to help you.

1. **Lava** is melted rock that has poured out of a volcano.
2. **Magma** is melted rock inside a volcano.
3. Magma builds up pressure inside a **magma chamber** inside the volcano.
4. When enough pressure builds up, melted rock, ash and gas come out through a **vent**, or opening, in the volcano. Often the pressure causes the vent to open.
5. As lava and ash cools on the outside of a vent, it builds into a **cone**.

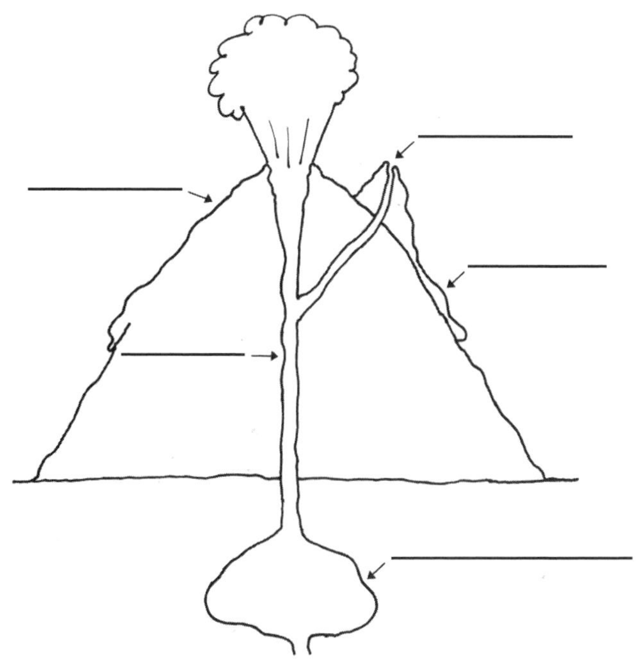

DAILY VOCABULARY PRACTICE

Geography Words

3

Name ______________________________

Match each word about volcanoes with its definition.

1. eruption	not active
2. volcanologist	melted rock inside the Earth; called lava outside
3. magma	an explosion
4. dormant	the shape of many volcanoes
5. cone	a person who studies volcanoes

geography words geography words
Week Twenty-Eight

DAILY VOCABULARY PRACTICE

Geography Words

4

Name ______________________________

Read each clue. Write the answer on the line.

1. not part of a piece of bread, but the Earth's outermost layer ______________
2. not the inside of an apple, but the very center of Earth ______________
3. not something above a fireplace, but the Earth's middle layer ______________
4. not the inside; another name for outside ______________
5. not the outside; another name for inside ______________

interior core crust mantle exterior

Geography Words

5

Name ____________________

Read each clue. Use the Word Bank. Write the answer on the line.

1. I look like a mountain but when I erupt, watch out! ____________
2. I'm a tsunami, a huge ____________ caused by an underwater earthquake.
3. I send rocks and earth toppling down mountainsides. ____________
4. I'm the result of shifting rock plates deep in the earth. ____________
5. I send huge piles of snow and ice sliding down a mountain. ____________

avalanche	earthquake	landslide	volcano	wave

Geography Words

Name ____________________

Circle the best word to complete each sentence.

1. Most of Antarctica is covered by **ice/water**.
2. A volcano that has not erupted in a long time is called **active/dormant**.
3. The innermost part of the earth is called the **mantle/core**.
4. The wave caused by an underwater earthquake is called a **tsunami/landslide**.
5. Melted rock inside a volcano is called **magma/lava**.

DAILY VOCABULARY PRACTICE

Name ____________________

A. Choose the best word to complete each sentence.

longitude
poles
Northeast
hemisphere
latitude

1. The United States and Canada are in the western ____________.
2. On a globe, lines of ____________ run north and south.
3. The equator, which runs east and west, is located at 0 degrees ____________.
4. New York, New Jersey, and Connecticut are located in the ____________.
5. Lines of longitude stretch between the ____________.

B. Find five geography words in the puzzle.

plateau dormant east mantle west

D	Y	W	E	D	P
O	R	E	L	B	L
R	A	S	T	X	A
M	U	T	N	J	T
A	T	U	A	I	E
N	S	V	M	Q	A
T	E	A	S	T	U

C. Complete the puzzle.

Across

1. I am a triangle of land where a river flows into the ocean.
4. I am a large part of an ocean or sea that is partially surrounded by land.
6. I am a deep valley with steep sides.

Down

2. I am a piece of land with water on three sides.
3. I am a ring-shaped coral island
5. I am the Earth's innermost section.

atoll canyon core delta gulf peninsula

DAILY VOCABULARY PRACTICE

Language Arts Words

1

Name ______________________________

Punctuation marks help you to communicate your ideas clearly in writing.

Choose the best word or term to complete each sentence.

1. Always use a ______________________ at the end of a statement.
2. Use a ______________________ at the end of a question.
3. End a sentence with an ______________________ if you want to show strong emotion.
4. Use an ______________________ in a contraction.
5. A ______________________ is used to separate items in a list or series.

comma	**period**	**question mark**	**exclamation point**	**apostrophe**

Week Twenty-Nine

DAILY VOCABULARY PRACTICE

Language Arts Words

Name ______________________________

Punctuation marks help you to communicate your ideas clearly in writing.

What is missing from each sentence? Circle the best answer. Then, add the missing punctuation.

1. Lisa and her mother went to the grocery store	period or comma
2. Do you want to know what was on their list	period or question mark
3. Milk juice and oranges were on the list.	exclamation point or commas
4. Lisa's mom added two more items eggs and bread.	semi-colon or colon
5. Juan cant come to the party.	period or apostrophe

DAILY VOCABULARY PRACTICE

Language Arts Words

3

Name ______________________________

Punctuation marks help you to communicate your ideas clearly in writing.

Label each punctuation mark.

1. ( ) ______________________________
2. : ______________________________
3. ; ______________________________
4. " " ______________________________
5. ? ______________________________

colon parentheses question mark quotation marks semicolon

language arts words literature punctuation words Week Twenty-Nine

DAILY VOCABULARY PRACTICE

Language Arts Words

Name ______________________________

Punctuation marks help you to communicate your ideas clearly in writing.

Read each clue. Write the answer on the line.

1. I am added to nouns to show possession. I am an ____________.
2. I am used to show that someone said something. I am ____________.
3. I can be used to introduce items in a series. I am a ____________.
4. I am used to separate parts of a sentence. I am a ____________.
5. I am used to separate the name of a city and state. I am a ____________.

apostrophe colon comma quotation marks semi-colon

Language Arts Words

5

Name ______________________________

Punctuation marks help you to communicate your ideas clearly in writing.

Read each sentence. Look for a punctuation or capitalization mistake. Then circle the correct solution.

1. Bears dogs, and wolves are mammals.	Add a comma	Add a period
2. dogs and wolves are related.	Use a capital letter	Use a lowercase letter
3. Do bears lay eggs	Add a period	Add a question mark
4. Don't be silly	Add a question mark	Add an exclamation point
5. Baby bears are called Cubs.	Use a lowercase letter	Use a capital letter

Language Arts Words

Name ______________________________

Write a sentence using each punctuation mark

1. period

____

2. apostrophe

____

3. colon

____

4. question mark

____

5. exclamation point

____

DAILY VOCABULARY PRACTICE

Language Arts Words

1

Name ______________________________

Look at each example below. Does it describe a work of fiction or nonfiction? Write your answer on the line.

1. A story about a child who travels back in time ______________
2. A magazine article about preventing sunburn ______________
3. A novel about a school for wizards ______________
4. A newspaper article about the Presidential election ______________
5. A play about the secret lives of cats ______________

language arts words literature punctuation words Week Thirty

DAILY VOCABULARY PRACTICE

Language Arts Words

2

Name ______________________________

There are many genres, or styles, of literature. For example, fiction and nonfiction are two genres. Look at the genres below. Use an X to mark the word or statement that does not describe the genre.

1. **fiction**	invented	made-up	true
2. **nonfiction**	factual	based on research	imagined
3. **poetry**	never read aloud	rhyming	rhythmic
4. **essay**	fictional	first-person experience	persuasive
5. **biography**	personal	rhyming	factual

Language Arts Words

3

Name ______________________________

Unscramble the terms below. Write the words on the lines. Check the word bank for clues.

1. hetem ______________________ the central idea of the story
2. topl ______________________ what happens
3. gstneti ______________________ where it happens
4. tcaahrecsr ______________________ who takes part
5. fcolintc ______________________ a struggle within the plot

conflict theme characters setting plot

Language Arts Words

Name ______________________________

Match each character to its genre.

1. Harry Potter — myth
2. Cinderella — fable
3. Fox (and the grapes) — fairy tales
4. Apollo, the Sun God — folk tale
5. Paul Bunyan — fantasy

DAILY VOCABULARY PRACTICE

Language Arts Words

5

Name ______________________________

Read the sentences below. They use similes and metaphors. A simile describes something by comparing it to something else. It often uses the words *like* and *as*. A metaphor describes something by calling it something else.

1. His teeth were like pearls.	simile	metaphor
2. The test was a bear!	simile	metaphor
3. The baby's skin was as soft as silk.	simile	metaphor
4. Don't be such a wet blanket—join the fun!	simile	metaphor
5. The city lights twinkled like stars.	simile	metaphor

DAILY VOCABULARY PRACTICE

Language Arts Words

Name ______________________________

Read each clue. Write the best answer on the line.

1. I am a story that comes from the author's imagination. ____________
2. I am a story based on a person's life ____________
3. I am the events in a story. ____________
4. I am a story passed down over time. I often try to explain things. ____________
5. I describe something by comparing it to something else. ____________

biography	**fiction**	**myth**	**plot**	**simile**

DAILY VOCABULARY PRACTICE

Language Arts Words

1

Name ________________________________

Put the steps of the writing process in the correct order.

1. _______ publish
2. _______ prewrite
3. _______ edit
4. _______ revise
5. _______ write

Week Thirty-One

DAILY VOCABULARY PRACTICE

Language Arts Words

2

Name ________________________________

Match each word with its definition.

1. author	produces the book
2. illustrator	helps the author to make ideas clear
3. editor	the person who enjoys the book in the end
4. publisher	provides drawings for the book
5. reader	writes the book

DAILY VOCABULARY PRACTICE

Language Arts Words

3

Name ______________________________

Complete each sentence by filling in the blank.

1. A dictionary lists words and their meanings in ________________ order.
2. Find a reference article about mammals in an ________________.
3. Find today's news in a ________________.
4. What's your friend's phone number? Check out the ________________ book.
5. Order a new pair of jeans from a mail-order ________________.

alphabetical catalog encyclopedia newspaper telephone

DAILY VOCABULARY PRACTICE

Language Arts Words

4

Name ______________________________

Books are organized to help you find information easily. Read each clue. Circle the part of the book that is being described.

1. I am in the front of the book. I tell you what's inside. What am I? ________________
2. I am usually in the back of the book. I define words. What am I? ________________
3. I am an alphabetical listing of subjects in the book. What am I? ________________
4. I name the story. What am I? ________________
5. You can usually find me next to photographs. I explain the pictures. What am I? ________________

caption glossary index table of contents title

Language Arts Words

5

Name ______________________________

Choose the best reference book for each situation.

1. You need to know a word's meaning. Choose a ______________.
2. You want to find a synonym for a word. Choose a ______________.
3. You are doing a research paper on the printing press. Choose an ______________.
4. You need a map of Europe. Choose an ______________.
5. You want to know the date of the next full moon. Choose an ______________.

almanac atlas dictionary encyclopedia thesaurus

Language Arts Words

Name ______________________________

**Unscramble each word. Write the word on the line.
Match it to the description.**

1. rsevie ______________ a book of synonyms
2. ouhrta ______________ a writer
3. persnewap ______________ place to find word definitions
4. ylossrag ______________ carries reports of important events
5. usuetsrah ______________ to make changes or rewrite

revise author glossary newspaper thesaurus

DAILY VOCABULARY PRACTICE

Language Arts Words

1

Name ______________________________

Do you know your poetry? Find out here.

Fill in the missing vowels.

1. h____ ____k____ (a 17-syllable poem about nature)
2. c____ ____pl ____t (a two-line rhyme)
3. c____nq____ ____ ____n (a five-line poem)
4. fr____ ____v____rs____ (a non-rhyming poem)
5. ____ cr____st____c (each line of the poem starts with a letter from the title)

acrostic couplet free verse haiku rhyme

language arts words literature punctuation words book
Week Thirty-Two

DAILY VOCABULARY PRACTICE

Language Arts Words

2

Name ______________________________

Use context clues and the word bank to help you complete each sentence.

1. To ______________________ means to explain the meaning of something.
2. To ______________________ means to talk with others.
3. To ______________________ means to argue the merits of a topic.
4. To ______________________ means to consider something's value.
5. To ______________________ means to think about something critically.

critique debate discuss evaluate interpret

DAILY VOCABULARY PRACTICE

Language Arts Words

3

Name ______________________________

Write the letter on the line that best matches the word.

____ 1. drama

____ 2. dialogue

____ 3. character

____ 4. comedy

____ 5. scene

a. part of a play

b. a role in a play

c. the words spoken in a play

d. a play about a serious subject

e. a funny play

DAILY VOCABULARY PRACTICE

Language Arts Words

4

Name ______________________________

Read the clues. Complete each sentence with a word from the word bank.

1. Jan wrote her best friend Dee a ____________________.
2. Mei Li checked out the headlines in the daily ____________________.
3. For her birthday Marilyn got a subscription to a monthly ____________________.
4. Juan found that he liked writing in his ____________________ every day after school.
5. The sports reporter was happy with answers to his questions in his ____________________ with the football quarterback.

interview journal letter magazine newspaper

DAILY VOCABULARY PRACTICE

Language Arts Words

5

Name ____________________

Complete the sentences with words from the word bank.

1. There are four kinds of ____________.
2. A ____________ sentence makes a statement.
3. An ____________ sentence asks a question.
4. An ____________ sentence expresses strong emotion.
5. An ____________ sentence gives a command or directions.

declarative	**exclamatory**	**imperative**	**interrogatory**	**sentences**

DAILY VOCABULARY PRACTICE

Language Arts Words

Name ____________________

Choose the best word to complete each sentence.

1. A ____________ is a 17-syllable poem.
2. In the ____________, the students argued for and against school uniforms.
3. In a play, realistic ____________ makes the characters believable.
4. The reporter asked tough questions in her ____________ with the president.
5. This is a ____________ sentence.

debate	**declarative**	**dialogue**	**interview**	**haiku**

Monthly Review 8

DAILY VOCABULARY PRACTICE

Name ______________________________

A. Circle the best answer.

1. a reference book with synonyms	thesaurus	glossary
2. source of definitions, in back of book	contents	glossary
3. a person in a book or play	caption	character
4. gives information about photos	caption	atlas
5. in a play, speech between characters	caption	dialogue

B. Write the words in alphabetical order, from top to bottom.

___ ___ ___ ___ ___ ___ ☐ ___ ___ ___ ___ ___

___ ___ ___ ___ ___ ☐ ___

☐ ___ ___ ___ ___ ___ ___ ___

___ ___ ___ ___ ☐ ___

___ ___ ___ ☐ ___ ___ ___

The letters in bold will spell out the answer to this riddle:

I make music, but I'm not an instrument. What am I?

____

memoir synonym almanac dialogue alliteration

C. Complete the puzzle. Find the words in the word bank in the puzzle below. Look across, down, up, backwards and diagonally.

fiction
haiku
critique
essay
debate
poetry
fantasy

Q	D	D	Q	K	S	N	P	Y	E
E	D	E	W	R	O	O	O	M	U
U	O	C	B	I	H	F	E	N	Q
F	A	N	T	A	S	Y	T	V	I
J	S	C	I	Q	T	Z	R	U	T
G	I	K	M	Y	Z	E	Y	E	I
F	U	Y	A	S	S	E	R	W	R
R	Y	A	M	I	V	E	P	I	C

Social Studies Words

1

Name ______________________________

The United States has a federal government.

Complete each sentence. Use context clues and the word bank for answers.

1. There are three branches of the federal ______________________.
2. The president, or chief executive, heads the ______________________ branch.
3. The Supreme Court and its judges are part of the ______________________ branch.
4. The ______________________ branch helps to make and pass laws, or legislation.
5. Thousands of other people work in jobs in these three ______________________.

branches	executive	government	judicial	legislative

Social Studies Words

2

Name ______________________________

The legislative branch of the United States government has two parts—the House of Representatives and the Senate. Together, they make the laws that make the government work. Complete the sentences with answers from the word bank.

1. The Senate has 100 elected members, called ______________________.
2. Members elected to the House of Representatives are called ______________________.
3. Together these two "houses" make up the ______________________.
4. A new law must get a majority of ______________________ in each house of Congress.
5. After a ______________________ is passed by Congress, it goes to the president to be signed.

law	representatives	senators	votes	U.S. Congress

DAILY VOCABULARY PRACTICE

Social Studies Words

3

Name ______________________________

Find the words from the bank in the puzzle. Look across and down.

L E G I S L A T E
A B O C T O D I L
W E R M A Y O R E
F L P X T E Q D C
B G O V E R N O R

governor	law	legislate	mayor	state

social studies words social studies words Week Thirty-Three

DAILY VOCABULARY PRACTICE

Social Studies Words

Name ______________________________

Read the clue. Write the best answer on the line. Check the word bank for clues.

1. I am the opposite of rejection. I rhyme with selection. ____________________
2. If I am 18, I can ____________________ in an election.
3. I am the person running for office. ____________________
4. Candidates ____________________ for peoples' votes.
5. I am a sheet of paper used to cast a vote. ____________________

ballot	candidate	campaign	election	vote

DAILY VOCABULARY PRACTICE

Social Studies Words

5

Name ________________________________

Read each sentence. Add the missing prefix or suffix to each word.

1. "No taxation without represent___ ___ ___ ___ ___."
2. The House of Represent___ ___ ___ ___ ___ ___ is part of the Congress.
3. To ___ ___ ___represent something is to not tell the whole truth.
4. The Congress today passed new legisl___ ___ ___ ___ ___.
5. A legisl ___ ___ ___ ___ is a person who makes laws.

-ator	-atives	-ation	-mis

DAILY VOCABULARY PRACTICE

Social Studies Words

Name ________________________________

Write the word on the line that best fits the definition.

1. a person who helps make laws ________________
2. a person running for political office ________________
3. one of the three branches of government ________________
4. government by the people ________________
5. the highest level of government in the U.S. ________________

candidate	legislator	federal	executive	democracy

DAILY VOCABULARY PRACTICE

Social Studies Words

1

Name ______________________________

Complete each sentence. Check the word bank for clues.

1. I am an elected member of the United States Senate. Each state elects two of me. I am a ____________________.
2. I have 50 members, two for each state. I am the U.S. ____________________.
3. My members include senators and representatives. I am the U.S. ____________________.
4. I have 435 members. I am the U.S. ____________________.
5. I am one of the 435 members of the House. I am a ____________________.

Senate	**House of Representatives**	**Congress**	**senator**	**representative**

social studies words social studies words Week Thirty-Four

DAILY VOCABULARY PRACTICE

Social Studies Words

2

Name ______________________________

Read each description. Circle the best answer.

1. the elected leader of the United States	president	governor
2. the elected leader of a state	mayor	governor
3. next in line to the presidency	mayor	vice president
4. the elected leader of a city or town	governor	mayor
5. A governor works in this branch of government.	judicial	executive

DAILY VOCABULARY PRACTICE

Social Studies Words

3

Name ______________________________

Unscramble each word. Write it on the line. Use the word box and the clues.

1. gejdu ____________________ presides in court
2. itsceuJ ____________________ member of Supreme Court
3. Spree moCruut ____________________ highest court in the land
4. ruyj ____________________ citizens who decide a case
5. tcuor ____________________ place where cases are heard

court judge jury justice Supreme Court

social studies words social studies words Week Thirty-Four

DAILY VOCABULARY PRACTICE

Social Studies Words

4

Name ______________________________

Complete each sentence.

1. In the United States there are two major ____________________ parties.
2. The donkey is the symbol of the Democratic ____________________.
3. An elephant is the symbol of the ____________________ party.
4. An ____________________ is not a member of the two major political parties.
5. A constituent is a person ____________________ by an elected official.

independent party political Republican represented

Social Studies Words

5

Name ______________________________

Match each abbreviation with the word or words that it stands for.

1. POTUS — Democrat
2. V.P. — Governor
3. Gov. — President of the United States
4. Rep. — Vice President
5. Dem. — Republican

Social Studies Words

Name ______________________________

Add the vowels to complete each word. Match the word to its definition.

1. S___n___t___r — the elected leader of a state
2. g___v___rn___r — member of U.S. Congress; each state has two
3. J___st___c___ — a person represented by an elected official
4. c___nst___t___ ___nt — one of two major political parties in the U.S.
5. D___m___cr___t — one of nine members of the Supreme Court

justice governor senator constituent Democrat

DAILY VOCABULARY PRACTICE

Social Studies Words

1

Name ______________________________

Read each word or term. Choose the best label from the word bank.

1. Hawthorne Elementary ____________________
2. Sherman Oaks ____________________
3. Arizona ____________________
4. Canada ____________________
5. Circle the synonym for country: city state nation

state	**school**	**country**	**community**

DAILY VOCABULARY PRACTICE

Social Studies Words

2

Name ______________________________

Many states divide themselves into smaller regions such as cities and counties.

Match the scrambled and unscrambled words.

1. ctuyno — city
2. ycti — borough
3. owtn — county
4. rpshai — town
5. ohuorbg — parish

DAILY VOCABULARY PRACTICE

Social Studies Words

3

Name ______________________

Write the matching state abbreviations on the line.

1. Delaware, Pennsylvania, New Jersey, Georgia ______________
2. Connecticut, Massachusetts, Maryland ______________
3. South Carolina, New Hampshire, Virginia ______________
4. New York, North Carolina, Rhode Island ______________
5. Texas, Vermont, California ______________

SC, NH, VA	CT, MA, MD	DE, PA, NJ, GA	NY, NC, RI	TX, VT, CA

social studies words social studies words Week Thirty-Five

DAILY VOCABULARY PRACTICE

Social Studies Words

4

Name ______________________

Write the word that best matches the definition.

1. typical of a city ______________
2. a smaller town or city outside a large urban center ______________
3. having to do with the country ______________
4. Which word best describes New York City? Circle one: suburban urban
5. Which word best describes most National Parks? Circle one: rural urban

urban suburb rural

DAILY VOCABULARY PRACTICE

Social Studies Words

5

Name ______________________________

Unscramble each word. Find its match on the right.

1. ilcaos — political (related to politics and government)
2. ilpioltca — economic (related to the use of money and the ecomomy)
3. lurcualt — social (related to how people get along in their society)
4. cncomoei — cultural (related to how groups of people live)
5. Which of these four words has to do with money and finance?

____

DAILY VOCABULARY PRACTICE

Social Studies Words

Name ______________________________

Read each riddle. Write the best answer on the line.

1. I have four syllables. I rhyme with unity. What am I? ______________________
2. Add the letter *r* to my name and I become something bigger. What am I?

   ____
3. I start with the letter *D*. I was the first state to join the Union.

   ____
4. I am the opposite of urban. What am I? ______________________
5. I have to do with money and finance. What am I? ______________________

county	**Delaware**	**community**	**economics**	**rural**

DAILY VOCABULARY PRACTICE

Social Studies Words

1

Name ______________________________

Match the synonyms.

1. attorney	village
2. community	elect
3. law	lawyer
4. town	neighborhood
5. vote	rule

DAILY VOCABULARY PRACTICE

Social Studies Words

2

Name ______________________________

Read each clue. Write the best answer.

1. having to do with law ______________
2. a lawmaker ______________
3. against the law ______________
4. to make something legal ______________
5. a lawmaking group ______________

legislature	**legal**	**illegal**	**legalize**	**legislator**

DAILY VOCABULARY PRACTICE

Social Studies Words

3

Name ______________________________

Circle the word that best matches each definition.

1. something to which you are entitled	law	right
2. a guideline	rule	privilege
3. a guideline enforced by the government	law	responsibility
4. a right	rule	privilege
5. a duty	law	responsibility

DAILY VOCABULARY PRACTICE

Social Studies Words

Name ______________________________

Choose the best word to complete each phrase.

1. Martin Luther King, Jr. fought for ____________________ rights.
2. Voting is a ____________________ duty.
3. Anyone born in the United States is a ____________________.
4. Pyramids were symbols of ancient Egyptian ____________________.
5. Circle the word that does not belong: coarse impolite gruff civilized

civic civilization citizen civil

DAILY VOCABULARY PRACTICE

Social Studies Words

5

Name ______________________________

Complete each quote with a word from the bank. You can use one word twice.

1. "Life, ________________, and the pursuit of happiness."
2. "...all men are created ________________."
3. "in order to form a more perfect ________________."
4. "With liberty and ________________ for all."
5. "My country 'tis of thee, sweet land of ________________, of thee I sing."

equal justice liberty union

DAILY VOCABULARY PRACTICE

Social Studies Words

Name ______________________________

Circle the best word to complete each sentence.

1. The U.S. Constitution/amendment was signed by the Founding Fathers.
2. A person who creates laws is called a legal/legislator.
3. A privilege/responsibility is a right.
4. An immigrant to the U.S. can apply for civilization/citizenship.
5. The Statue of Justice/Liberty is in New York City.

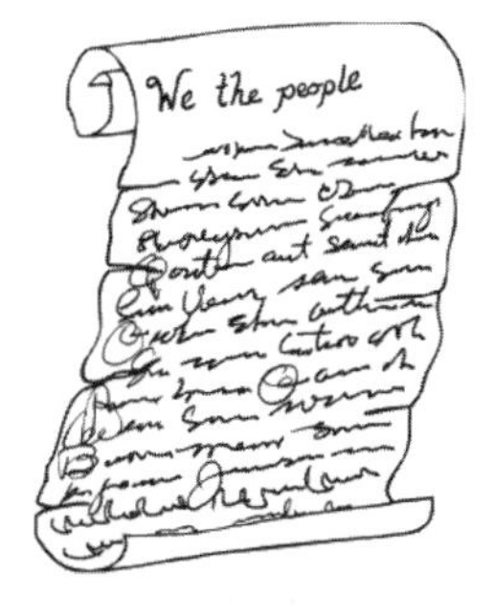

DAILY VOCABULARY PRACTICE

Name ______________________________

A. Choose the best word to complete each sentence.

1. The highest court in the land is the _______________ Court.
2. The leader of the United States is the _______________.
3. A senator is a member of _______________
4. The head of a city government is its _______________.
5. Next in line to the president is the _______________ president.

Congress	**mayor**	**president**	**Supreme**	**vice**

B. Circle the word that doesn't belong in each row

1. senator	mayor	president	law
2. community	town	debate	city
3. judge	basketball	court	law
4. party	jury	candidate	vote
5. rule	guideline	law	play

C. Complete the puzzle.

Across

1. The United States has two main _____________ parties.
5. The United States _____________ is a set of laws.
6. It is against the _____________ to drive through a red light.
7. Who will you _____________ for on Election Day?

Down

2. The mayor is a leader in _____________ government.
3. The president is head of the _____________ branch.
4. In 1959, Hawaii became the 50th _____________.

vote political law executive Constitution state local

Daily Vocabulary Practice

Answers — Grade 4

Pp. 6–8, Week 1

Day 1: 1. yes; 2. yes; 3. no; 4. no; 5. yes

Day 2: 1. park → Yosemite National Park; 2. street → Main Street; 3. building → Empire State Building; 4. hospital → St. Luke's Medical Center; 5. train station → Grand Central Station

Day 3: 1. underline *Mr. Gonzalez,* circle *teacher*; 2. circle *school*, underline *Learning Academy*; 3. underline *Mr. Gonzalez*, circle *students* and *class*; 4. circle *class*, underline *Native Americans*; 5. circle *Students*, underline *Navajo Indians*

Day 4: 1. September; 2. December; 3. January; 4. March; 5. June

Day 5: 1. beauty; 2. peace; 3. intelligence; 4. love; 5. honesty

Weekly Review: 1. Arizona; 2. Golden Delicious; 3. Arctic; 4. Vesuvius; 5. J. K. Rowling

Pp. 9–11, Week 2

Day 1: 1. yes; 2. yes; 3. no; 4. no; 5. yes

Day 2: 1. snap; 2. beat; 3. tap; 4. sing; 5. clap

Day 3: 1. visit; 2. demonstrate; 3. teach; 4. search; 5. decide

Day 4: 1. support; 2. identify; 3. realize; 4. comprehend; 5. observe

Day 5: 1. noun; 2. verb; 3. verb; 4. noun; 5. verb

Weekly Review: 1. Circle *consider*; 2. Circle *increase* and *runs*; 3. Circle *distribute*; 4. Circle *volunteers* and *read*; 5. Circle *imagine* and *will be*

Pp. 12–14, Week 3

Day 1: 1. underline *delicious*; 2. underline *Italian*; 3. underline *crusty* and *crunchy*; 4. underline *curly* and *chunky*; 5. underline *sweet* and *creamy*

Day 2: 1. hilarious → a funny bunny; 2. beautiful → a pretty city; 3. curious → an eager beaver; 4. independent → a free bee; 5. improved → a better letter

Day 3: 1. clever → smart; 2. anxious → worried; 3. ecstatic → happy; 4. cooperative → helpful; mischievous → playful

Day 4: 1. bulky; 2. microscopic; 3. Massive; 4. immense; 5. miniature

Day 5: 1. delicious; 2. ridiculous; 3. ancient; 4. modern; 5. insistent

Weekly Review: 1. weary; 2. original; 3. vast; 4. enormous; 5. reliable

Pp. 15–18 Week 4

Day 1: 1. elegantly; 2. faithfully; 3. courageously; 4. successfully; 5. innocently

Day 2: 1. hourly; 2. daily; 3. weekly; 4. monthly; 5. yearly

Day 3: 1. underline *galloped*, circle *swiftly*; 2. underline *approached*, circle *slowly*; 3. underline *jumped*, circle *playfully*; 4. underline *nibbled*, circle *happily*; 5. underline *slept*, circle *peacefully*

Day 4: 1. extremely; 2. thoroughly; 3. frequently; 4. conveniently; 5. promptly

Day 5: 1. Josh is *occasionally* late for school.; 2. Help is *urgently* needed.; 3. The shirt is *permanently* stained.; 4. Most students worked *independently*.; 5. The parents met with the teacher *briefly*.

Weekly Review: 1. mysteriously; 2. adoringly; 3. energetically; 4. serenely; 5. decisively

Monthly Review: A. 1. adjective; 2. noun; 3. adverb; 4. verb; 5. adjective;

B.

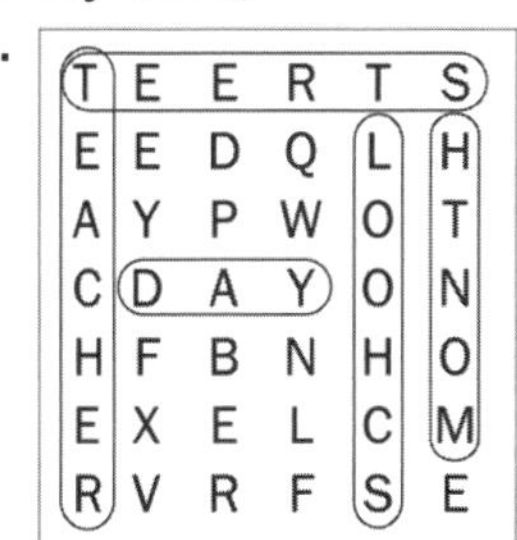

C.

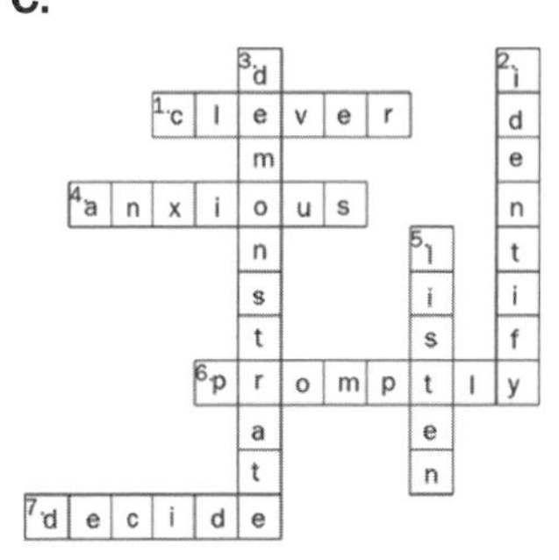

Pp. 19–21, Week 5

Day 1: 1. rewrite; 2. reassemble; 3. rearrange; 4. reconstruct; 5. rediscover

Day 2: 1. impossible; 2. impolite; 3. indecisive; 4. independent; 5. immature

Day 3: 1. misjudge; 2. misinform; 3. misbehave; 4. mistake; 5. miscount

Day 4: 1. decathlon; 2. triplets; 3. unicycle; 4. centennial; 5. bicycle

Day 5: 1. antisocial; 2. postpone; 3. microscope; 4. midnight; 5. triangle

Weekly Review: 1. re–; 2. im–; 3. mis–; 4. bi–; 5. anti–

Pp. 22–24, Week 6

Day 1: 1. playful; 2. quickly, quickness, quickest; 3. helpful, helpless; 4. restful, restless; 5. hardly, hardness, hardest

Day 2: 1. briefer, briefest; 2. later, latest; 3. nearer, nearest; 4. higher, highest; 5. faster, fastest

Day 3: 1. creative; 2. detective; 3. massive; 4. impressive; 5. relative

Day 4: 1. –ly; 2. –ly; 3. –ness; 4. –ment; 5. –ful

Day 5: 1. combination; 2. narration; 3. definition; 4. operation; 5. invitation

Weekly Review: 1. underline *able, ment*; 2. underline *ly, ness*; 3. underline *ize, able*; 4. underline *ize, ness*; 5. underline *ly, ness*

Pp. 25–27, Week 7

Day 1: 1. note/book; 2. key/board; 3. down/load; 4. desk/top; 5. pass/word

Day 2: 1. pancake; 2. strawberry; 3. meatball; 4. popcorn; 5. basketball

Day 3: 1. daydream; 2. seashell; 3. newspaper; 4. playground; 5. downpour

Day 4: 1. fore → head, forehead; finger → nail, fingernail; eye → ball, eyeball; 4. back → bone, backbone; 5. knee → cap, kneecap

Day 5: 1. another; 2. anywhere; 3. meanwhile; 4. sometimes; 5. somewhat

Weekly Review: 1. nail; 2. walk; 3. back; 4. quarters; 5. light

Pp. 28–30, Week 8

Day 1: 1. clear; 2. use; 3. pain; 4. king; 5. prove

Day 2: 1. explanation → explain; 2. confusion → confuse; 3. action → act; 4. formation → form; 5. precaution → caution

Day 3: 1. clearly; 2. triumphant; 3. beautiful; 4. electricity; 5. representative

Day 4: 1. union; 2. relate; 3. teach; 4. distinct; 5. embarrass

Day 5: 1. decide; 2. produce; 3. add; 4. correct; 5. complete

Weekly Review: 1. complete, possible answers include *completely, completing*; 2. act, possible answers include *action, inaction*; 3. embarrass, possible answers include *embarrassment, embarrassed*; 4. add, possible answers include *additional, additive*; 5. meaning, possible answers include *meaningful*

Monthly Review: A. 1. rearrange; 2. postpone; 3. agreement; 4. indecisive; 5. memorable; **B.** daydream; download; meanwhile; meatball; playground;

C.

Pp. 32–34, Week 9

Day 1: 1. yes; 2. yes; 3. no; 4. yes; 5. no

Day 2: 1. hideous; 2. shout; 3. bland; 4. sleepy; 5. loss

Day 3: 1. slow; 2. silent; 3. wee; 4. scarce; 5. punctual

Day 4: 1. jumbo → shrimp; 2. exact → estimate; 3. same → difference; 4. old → news; 5. never → again

Day 5: 1. interior, exterior; 2. departs, arrive; 3. innocent, guilty; 4. defense, offense; 5. past, future

Weekly Review: 1. Circle *repulsive*; 2. Circle *plain*; 3. Circle *wee*; 4. Circle *arrive*; 5. Circle *outside*

P. 35–37, Week 10

Day 1: 1. hard → challenging; 2. bad → horrible; 3. big → enormous; 4. small → miniscule; 5. weird → unusual

Day 2: 1. observe; 2. exclaim; 3. savor; 4. comprehend; 5. inhale

Day 3: 1. sparse; 2. ungrateful; 3. mean; 4. stingy; 5. fast

Day 4: 1. celebrate; 2. occurred; 3. ate; 4. traditional; 5. gather

Day 5: 1. allow, permit; 2. call, shout; 3. cure, heal; 4. grab, seize; 5. right, correct

Weekly Review: 1. Circle *no*; 2. Circle *yes*; 3. Circle *no*; 4. Circle *yes*; 5. Circle *no*

Pp. 38–40, Week 11

Day 1: 1. → bat; 2. → top; 3. → toast; 4. → ring; 5. → seal

Day 2: 1. d; 2. a; 3. c; 4. e; 5. b

Day 3: 1. temple; 2. squash; 3. tip; 4. watch; 5. lock

Day 4: 1. mouse; 2. screen; 3. lumber; 4. foil; 5. monitor

Day 5: 1. frank frank; 2. husky husky; 3. pupil's pupil; 4. school school; 5. firm firm

Weekly Review: 1. file; 2. bark; 3. bear; 4. cobbler; 5. date

Pp. 41–43; Week 12

Day 1: 1. flower → flour; clothes → close; 3. beet → beat; 4. bow → bough; 5. knight → night

Day 2: 1. current currant; 2. coarse course; 3. bare bear; 4. pair of pears; 5. pale pail

Day 3: 1. stake; 2. waste; 3. whole; 4. peace; 5. straight

Day 4: 1. circle *guest*, guessed; 2. circle *hour*, our; 3. circle *weave*, we've; 4. circle *knead*, need; 5. circle *foreword*, forward

Day 5: 1. aloud; 2. presents; 3. principle; 4. capital; 5. instants

Weekly Review: 1. Circle *attendants*; 2. Circle *basis*; 3. Circle *shoot*; 4. Circle *duel*; 5. Circle *lichen*

Monthly Review: A. 1. Circle *synonym*; 2. Circle *antonym*; 3. Circle *antonym*; 4. Circle *synonym*; 5. Circle *antonym*;

B.

S	E	A	P	D	B
T	C	L	E	E	A
S	E	L	A	S	L
E	I	O	C	S	O
U	P	W	E	E	U
G	R	E	B	U	D
P	T	D	Z	G	G

C.

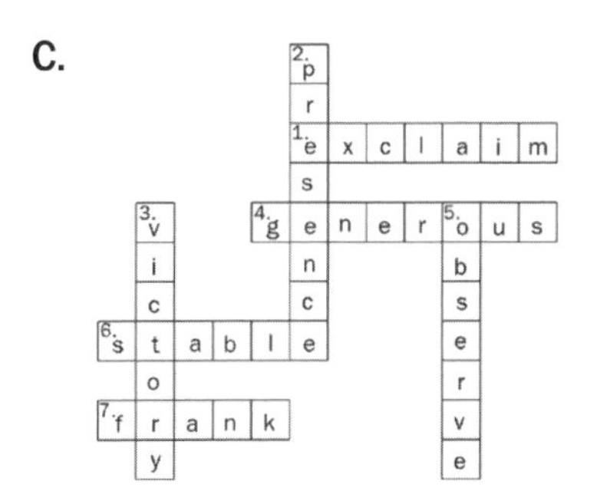

Pp. 45–47, Week 13

Day 1: 1. pop → popular; 2. ad → advertisement; 3. doc → doctor; 4. phone → telephone; 5. gas → gasoline

Day 2: 1. stats; 2. ref; 3. gym; 4. champ; 5. fan

Day 3: 1. **lab**oratory; 2. **exam**ination; 3. **math**ematics; 4. **dorm**itory; 5. **prof**essor

Day 4: 1. e; 2. d; 3. b; 4. a; 5. c

Day 5: 1. photo; 2. tux; 3. teen; 4. grad; 5. prom

Weekly Review: 1. advertisement/ad; 2. gymnasium/gym; 3. mathematics/math; 4. airplane/plane; 5. teenager/teen

Pp. 48–50, Week 14

Day 1: 1. twirl; 2. waddle; 3. flop; 4. splurge; 5. twiddle

Day 2: 1. brash; 2. snazzy; 3. humongous; 4. chump; 5. ditsy

Day 3: 1. blurt → blow and spurt; 2. chortle → chuckle and snort; 3. hassle → haggle and tussle; 4. squash → squeeze and crash; 5. squiggle → squeeze and wriggle

Day 4: 1. pluot; 2. brunch; 3. craisin; 4. spork; 5. tangelo

Day 5: 1. boost; 2. clash; 3. bleep; 4. flush; 5. smash

Weekly Review: 1. splash, surge; 2. huge, enormous; 3. chuckle, snort; 4. breakfast, lunch; 5. clap, crash

Pp. 51–53, Week 15

Day 1: 1. Internet → network between computers; 2. emoticon → smiley; 3. blog →Web log; 4. netiquette → internet etiquette; 5. e-mail → electronic mail

Day 2: 1. IMHO; 2. TTYL; 3. BTW; 4. OTOH; 5. LOL

Day 3: 1. mesmerize; 2. saxophone; 3. leotard; 4. sandwich; 5. silhouette

Day 4: 1. snail mail; 2. spam; 3. Google; 4. blog; 5. blogger

Day 5: 1. radar; 2. laser; 3. scuba; 4. sonar

Weekly Review: 1. Internet; 2. BTW; 3. mesmerize; 4. blog; 5. laser

Pp. 54–56, Week 16

Day 1: 1. transform; 2. exclaim; 3. spectator; 4. evacuate; 5. interrupt

Day 2: 1. manufacture; 2. biography; 3. thermometer; 4. cosmopolitan; 5. manuscript

Day 3: 1. cereal; 2. electricity; 3. volcano; 4. amazonian; 5. hygiene

Day 4: 1. banana; 2. artichoke; 3. tofu; 4. cookie; 5. bologna

Day 5: 1. cashmere, a soft wool → Kashmir, India; 2. cologne, a perfume → Cologne, Germany; 3. manila, a kind of paper → Manila, Philippines; 4. tangerine, a citrus fruit → Tangiers, Morocco; 5. muslin, a fabric; Mosul, Iraq

Weekly Review: 1. evacuate; 2. thermometer; 3. electricity; 4. bologna; 5. tangerine

Monthly Review: A. 1. fan; 2. photos; 3. leotard; 4. blog; 5. laser; **B.** 1. clap, crash; 2. splash, surge; 3. breakfast, lunch; 4. huge, monstrous; 5. squirm, wriggle;

C.

Pp. 58–60, Week 17

Day 1: 1. ocean; 2. desert; 3. forest; 4. grassland; 5. wetland

Day 2: 1. blizzard; 2. tornado; 3. hurricane; 4. drought; 5. thunderstorm

Day 3: 1. clim**ate**; 2. **at**mosph**ere**; 3. temper**ature**; 4. **ozone**; 5. weather

Day 4: 1. temperature; 2. degrees; 3. Fahrenheit; 4. Celsius; 5. barometer

Day 5: 1. environment, the natural world; 2. habitat, the home territory of a living thing; 3. pollution, dirtying of the soil, air, or water; 4. litter, trash; 5. ecology, the study of the natural world.

Weekly Review: 1. grassland/area covered with grass; 2. drought/period without rain; 3. climate/typical weather conditions; 4. temperature/a measure of hot or cold; 5. erosion/wearing away of earth

Pp. 61–63, Week 18

Day 1: 1. true; 2. false; 3. false; 4. true; 5. true

Day 2: 1. herbivore; 2. carnivore; 3. omnivore; 4. herbivore; 5. omnivore

Day 3: 1. mammal; 2. amphibian; 3. reptile; 4. insect; 5. bird

Day 4: 1. egg; 2. caterpillar; 3. chrysalis; 4. butterfly; 5. life cycle

Day 5: 1. circle *habbutat*, habitat; 2. circle *mygreat*, migrate; 3. circle *cammoflaj*, camouflage; 4. circle *hybernayt*, hibernate; 5. circle *indanjered*, endangered

Weekly Review: 1. Circle *vertebrates*; 2. Circle *carnivore*; 3. Circle *mammals*; 4. Circle *camouflage*; 5. Circle *life cycle*

Pp. 64–66, Week 19

Day 1: 1. heart; 2. stomach; 3. bones; 4. brain; 5. muscles

Day 2: enamel → the hardest substance in the human body; the surface of the tooth; 2. floss → a way to clean between teeth; 3. cavity → a diseased tooth has one; 4. brush → the first thing you do to clean your teeth; 5. gums → they keep your teeth secure.

Day 3: 1. nutrition; 2. protein; 3. grains; 4. vitamins; 5. energy

Day 4: 1. check-up; 2. vaccinations; 3. vision; 4. stethoscope; 5. throat

Day 5: 1. disease; 2. contagious; 3. chronic; 4. germ; 5. symptom

Weekly Review: 1. enamel; 2. nutrition 3. germ; 4. muscles; 5. stethoscope

Pp. 67–69, Week 20

Day 1: 1. Saturn; 2. Venus; 3. Neptune 4. Earth; 5. Mercury

Day 2: 1. solar; 2. sun; 3. orbit; 4. planets; 5. Milky Way

Day 3: 1. star; 2. planet; 3. comet; 4. meteor; 5. moon

Day 4: 1. circle *astronot*, astronaut; 2. circle *galacsy*, galaxy; 3. circle *gravitee*, gravity; 4. circle *unavers*, universe; 5. circle *spays*, space

Day 5: 1. observatory → an observation center; 2. constellation → a group of stars; 3. astronomy → the study of objects in space; 4. telescope → a tool used to see into space; 5. astronomer → a scientist who studies objects in space

Weekly Review: 1. Earth; 2. solar; 3. asteroid; 4. gravity; 5. constellation

Monthly Review: A. Space Science: constellation, astronomy, astronomer; Earth Science: drought, erosion, climate;

B. chronic; communicable; consumer; floss; invertebrate; Answer: Rumor;

C.

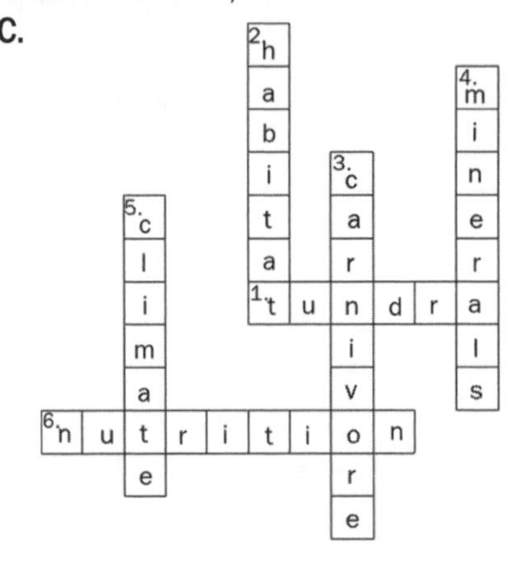

Pp. 71–73, Week 21

Day 1: 1. subtraction; 2. multiplication; 3. division; 4. addition; 5. division

Day 2: 1. problem; 2. different; 3. letter; 4. remove; 5. exact

Day 3: 1. multidigit; 2. prime; 3. odd; 4. even; 5. negative

Day 4: 1. convert; 2. determine; 3. decrease; 4. increase; 5. extend

Day 5: 1. strategy; 2. estimate; 3. computation; 4. approximate; 5. reasonable

Weekly Review: 1. multiplication; 2. equivalent; 3. negative; 4. strategy; 5. increase

Pp. 74–76, Week 22

Day 1: 1. triangle; 2. rectangle; 3. circle; 4. hexagon; 5. octagon

Day 2: 1. cylinder; 2. pyramid; 3. cone; 4. sphere; 5. cube

Day 3: 1. triangle; 2. rectangle; 3. square; 4. pentagon; 5. hexagon

Day 4: 1. triangle; 2. quadrilateral; 3. pentagon; 4. hexagon; 5. octagon

Day 5: 1. parallel; 2. distance; 3. circle; 4. center; 5. width

Weekly Review: 1. pyramid; 2. cylinder; 3. triangle; 4. hexagon; 5. parallel lines

Pp. 77–79, Week 23

Day 1: 1. inch → in; 2. foot → ft.; 3. ounce → oz.; 4. mile → mi.; 5. pound → lb.

Day 2: 1. cup; 2. pint; 3. ounces; 4. quart; 5. gallon

Day 3: 1. thermometer; 2. scale; 3. tape measure; 4. customary ruler; 5. metric ruler

Day 4: 1. c; 2. e; 3. a; 4. b; 5. d

Day 5: 1. mile; 2. pound; 3. cup; 4. liter; 5. gram

Weekly Review: 1. Circle *pounds*; 2. Circle *metric ruler*; 3. Circle *ounces*; 4. Circle *meter*; 5. Circle *volume*

Pp. 80–82, Week 24

Day 1: 1. fraction; 2. numerator; 3. denominator; 4. common; 5. simplify

Day 2: 1. quarter; 2. two-thirds; 3. half; 4. three-eighths; 5. whole

Day 3: 1. equivalent; 2. convert; 3. improper fraction; 4. proper fraction; 5. prime

Day 4: 1. decimal; 2. point; 3. digits; 4. round; 5. value

Day 5: 1. tenths; 2. thousandths; 3. hundred thousandths; 4. ten thousandths; 5. hundredths

Weekly Review: 1. simplify; 2. whole; 3. convert; 4. digit; 5. thousandths

Monthly Review: A. 1. equivalent; 2. numerator; 3. denominator; 4. converted ; 5. decimal;
B. Geometry Words: cylinder, line, rectangle; Measurement Words: kilometer, mile, ounce;
C.

T	A	E	M	M	I	T	S	E	Q
U	R	N	E	G	A	T	I	V	E
E	O	P	X	P	R	I	M	E	S
O	Q	T	P	A	A	O	P	O	T
P	E	X	T	E	N	D	L	T	I
T	M	E	S	A	O	C	I	Y	M
D	G	W	O	A	N	E	F	S	A
Y	F	Z	R	P	F	Z	Y	Y	T
G	E	O	M	E	T	R	Y	E	E
R	Z	C	K	I	E	V	V	X	T

Pp. 84–86, Week 25

Day 1: 1. map; 2. cartographer; 3. globe; 4. atlas; 5. geography

Day 2: 1. hemisphere; 2. equator; 3. longitude; 4. latitude; 5. pole

Day 3: 1. C; 2. E; 3. D; 4. A; 5. B

Day 4: 1. compass rose; 2. scale; 3. symbol; 4. borders; 5. key

Day 5: 1. Atlantic; 2. Pacific; 3. Indian; 4. Arctic; 5. Southern

Weekly Review: 1. cartographer; 2. hemisphere; 3. political map; 4. compass rose; 5. Atlantic

Pp. 87–89, Week 26

Day 1: 1. North; 2. South; 3. East; 4. West; 5. cardinal

Day 2: 1. Northwest → NW; 2. Southeast → SE; 3. Northeast → NE; 4. Southwest → SW; 5. intermediate

Day 3: 1. c; 2. d; 3. a; 4. b; 5. e

Day 4: 1. North Carolina; 2. West Virginia; 3. North Dakota; 4. South Dakota; 5. South Carolina

Day 5: 1. North; 2. South; 3. North; 4. South; 5. South

Weekly Review: 1. N → North; 2. NE → Northeast; 3. SW → Southwest; 4. S → South; 5. NW → Northwest

Pp. 90–92; Week 27

Day 1: swamp; 2. mountain; 3. cave; 4. hill; 5. glacier

Day 2: 1. Africa; 2. Europe; 3. Asia; 4. Oceania; 5. Antarctica; Extra: North America, South America

Day 3: 1. mountain; 2. desert; 3. plateau; 4. valley; 5. canyon

Day 4: 1. coast; 2. delta; 3. cape; 4. gulf; 5. cove

Day 5: 1. island; 2. archipelago; 3. peninsula; 4. isthmus; 5. atoll

Weekly Review: 1. plateau → an area of land that is flat and high; 2. Europe → one of the seven continents on Earth; 3. canyon → a deep valley with steep sides; 4. delta → triangle of land where a river flows into the ocean; 5. archipelago → a group of small islands

Pp. 93–95, Week 28

Day 1: 1. waves; 2. wind; 3. water; 4. ice; 5. surface

Day 2:

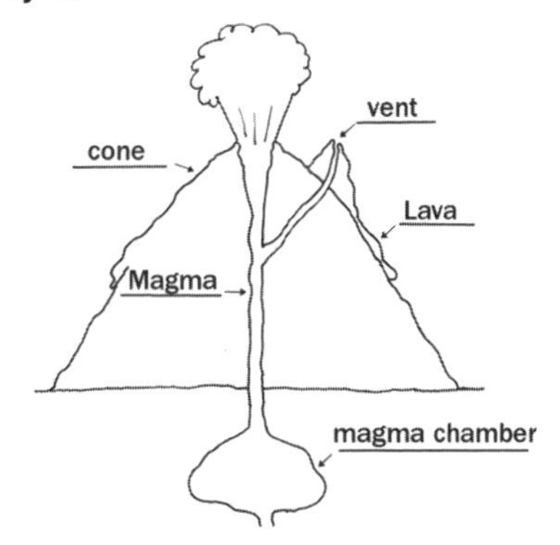

Day 3: 1. an explosion; 2. person who studies volcanoes; 3. melted rock; 4. not active; 5. shape of many volcanoes

Day 4: 1. crust; 2. core; 3. mantle; 4. exterior; 5. interior

Day 5: 1. volcano; 2. wave; 3. landslide; 4. earthquake; 5. avalanche

Weekly Review: 1. Circle *ice*; 2. Circle *dormant*; 3. Circle *core*; 4. Circle *tsunami*; 5. Circle *magma*

Monthly Review: A. 1. hemisphere; 2. longitude; 3. latitude; 4. Northeast; 5. poles

B.

C.

	2. p				
1. d	e	l	t	3. a	
	n			t	
	i			o	
	n			l	
	s			l	
4. g	u	l	f		
	l			5. c	
6. c	a	n	y	o	n
				r	
				e	

Pp. 97–99, Week 29

Day 1: 1. period; 2. question mark; 3. exclamation point; 4. apostrophe; 5. comma

Day 2: 1. Circle *period*; 2. Circle *question mark*; 3. Circle *commas*; 4. Circle *colon*; 5. Circle *apostrophe*

Day 3: 1. parentheses; 2. colon; 3. semicolon; 4. quotation mark; 5. question mark

Day 4: 1. apostrophe; 2. quotation marks; 3. colon; 4. semicolon; 5. comma

Day 5: 1. Circle *Add a comma*; 2. Circle *Use a capital letter*; 3. Circle *Add a question mark*; 4. Circle *Add an exclamation point*; 5. Circle *Use a lowercase letter*

Weekly Review: Answers will vary.

Pp. 100–102, Week 30

Day 1: 1. fiction; 2. nonfiction; 3. fiction; 4. nonfiction; 5. fiction

Day 2: 1. true; 2. imagined; 3. never read aloud; 4. fictional; 5. rhyming

Day 3: 1. theme; 2. plot; 3. setting; 4. characters; 5. conflict

Day 4: 1. fantasy; 2. fairy tale; 3. fable; 4. myth; 5. folk tale

Day 5: 1. Circle *simile*; 2. Circle *metaphor*; 3. Circle *simile*; 4. Circle *metaphor*; 5. Circle *simile*

Weekly Review: 1. fiction; 2. biography; 3. plot; 4. myth; 5. simile

Pp. 103–105, Week 31

Day 1: 1. prewrite; 2. write; 3. edit; 4. revise; 5. publish

Day 2: 1. author → writes the book; 2. illustrator → provides drawings for the book; 3. editor → helps the author to make ideas clear; 4. publisher → produces the book; 5. reader → the person who enjoys the book in the end

Day 3: 1. alphabetical; 2. encyclopedia; 3. newspaper; 4. phone; 5. catalog

Day 4: 1. table of contents; 2. glossary; 3. index; 4. title; 5. caption

Day 5: 1. dictionary; 2. thesaurus; 3. encyclopedia; 4. atlas; 5. almanac

Weekly Review: 1. revise ⟶ to make changes or rewrite; 2. author ⟶ a writer; 3. newspaper ⟶ carries reports of important events; 4. glossary ⟶ place to find word definitions; 5. thesaurus ⟶ a book of synonyms

Pp. 106–108, Week 32

Day 1: 1. haiku; 2. couplet; 3. cinquain; 4. free verse; 5. acrostic

Day 2: 1. interpret; 2. discuss; 3. debate; 4. evaluate; 5. critique

Day 3: 1. d; 2. c; 3. b; 4. e; 5. a

Day 4: 1. letter; 2. newspaper; 3. magazine; 4. journal; 5. interview

Day 5: 1. sentences; 2. declarative; 3. interrogative; 4. exclamatory; 5. imperative

Weekly Review: 1. haiku; 2. debate; 3. dialogue; 4. interview; 5. declarative

Monthly Review: A. 1. Circle *thesaurus*; 2. Circle *glossary*; 3. Circle *character*; 4. Circle *caption*; 5. Circle *dialogue*; **B.** alliteration; almanac; dialogue; memoir; synonym

C.

Q	D	D	Q	K	S	N	P	Y	E
E	D	E	W	R	O	O	O	M	U
U	O	C	B	I	H	F	E	N	Q
F	A	N	T	A	S	Y	T	V	I
J	S	C	I	Q	T	Z	R	U	T
G	I	K	M	Y	Z	E	Y	E	I
F	U	Y	A	S	S	E	R	W	R
R	Y	A	M	I	V	E	P	I	C

Pp. 110–112, Week 33

Day 1: 1. government; 2. executive; 3. judicial; 4. legislative; 5. branches

Day 2: 1. senators; 2. representatives; 3. U.S. Congress; 4. votes; 5. law

Day 3:

L	E	G	I	S	L	A	T	E
A	B	O	C	T	O	D	I	L
W	E	R	M	A	Y	O	R	E
F	L	P	X	T	E	Q	D	C
B	G	O	V	E	R	N	O	R

Day 4: 1. election; 2. vote; 3. candidate; 4. campaign; 5. ballot

Day 5: 1. –ation; 2. –atives; 3. mis- ; 4. –ation; 5. –ator

Weekly Review: 1. legislator; 2. candidate; 3. executive; 4. democracy; 5. federal

Pp. 113–115, Week 34

Day 1: 1. Senator; 2. Senate; 3. Congress; 4. House of Representatives; 5. Representative

Day 2: 1. Circle *president*; 2. Circle *governor*; 3. Circle *vice president*; 4. Circle *mayor*; 5. Circle *executive*

Day 3: 1. judge; 2. Justice; 3. Supreme Court; 4. jury; 5. court

Day 4: 1. political; 2. party; 3. Republican; 4. Independent; 5. represented

Day 5: 1. POTUS ⟶ President of the United States; 2. V.P. ⟶ Vice President; 3. Gov. ⟶ Governor; 4. Rep. ⟶ Republican; 5. Dem. ⟶ Democrat

Weekly Review: 1. Senator ⟶ Member of U.S. Congress; each state has two; 2. governor ⟶ The elected leader of a state; 3. Justice ⟶ One of nine members of the Supreme Court; 4. constituent ⟶ a person represented by an elected official; 5. Democratic ⟶ One of two major political parties in the U.S.

Pp. 116–117, Week 35

Day 1: 1. school; 2. community; 3. state; 4. country; 5. circle *nation*

Day 2: 1. county; 2. city; 3. town; 4. parish; 5. borough

Day 3: 1. DE, PA, NJ, GA; 2. CT, MA, MD; 3. SC, NH, VA; 4. NY, NC, RI; 5. TX, VT, CA

Day 4: 1. urban; 2. suburb; 3. rural; 4. urban; 5. rural

Day 5: 1. social; 2. political; 3. cultural; 4. economic; 5. economic

Weekly Review: 1. community; 2. county; 3. Delaware; 4. rural; 5. economics

Pp. 118–121, Week 36

Day 1: 1. lawyer; 2. neighborhood; 3. rule; 4. village; 5. elect

Day 2: 1. legal; 2. legislator; 3. illegal; 4. legalize; 5. legislature

Day 3: 1. Circle *right*; 2. Circle *rule*; 3. Circle *law*; 4. Circle *privilege*; 5. Circle *responsibility*

Day 4: 1. civil; 2. civic; 3. citizen; 4. civilization; 5. Circle *civilized*

Day 5: 1. liberty; 2. equal; 3. union; 4. justice; 5. liberty

Weekly Review: 1. Circle *U.S. Constitution*; 2. Circle *legislator*; 3. Circle *privilege*; 4. Circle *citizenship*; 5. Circle *Liberty*

Monthly Review: A. 1. Supreme; 2. president; 3. Congress; 4. mayor; 5. vice **B.** 1. law; 2. debate; 3. basketball; 4. jury; 5. play

C.

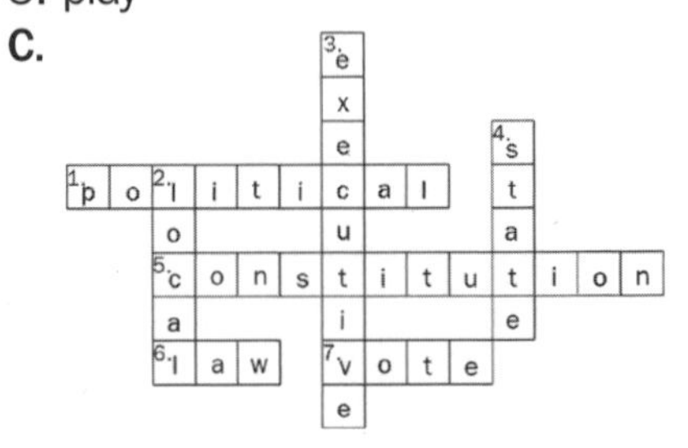